NatWest Business Handbo

This series has been written by a te
experience and are still actively ir
the small business.

If you are running a small business
business, you have no time for the general, theoretical and often inessential
detail of many business and management books. You need practical, readily
accessible, easy-to-follow advice which relates to your own working
environment and the problems you encounter. The NatWest Business
Handbooks fulfil these needs.

- They concentrate on specific areas which are particularly problematic
  to the small business.

- They adopt a step-by-step approach to the implementation of sound
  business skills.

- They offer practical advice on how to tackle problems.

The author

Alison Broadhurst has a Doctorate in Safety Administration, is a barrister (non-practising) and former HM Inspector of Factories and university business school lecturer. She has been for some years an independent safety consultant.

NatWest Business Handbooks

Health and Safety

Alison Broadhurst, PhD Barrister

Pitman Publishing
128 Long Acre, London WC2E 9AN
A Division of Longman Group UK Limited

First published in Great Britain in association with the National Westminster Bank,
1991
Reprinted 1991

© Longman Group UK Ltd 1991

British Library Cataloguing in Publication Data

Broadhurst, Alison
    Health and safety. – (NatWest business handbooks).
    1. Great Britain. Industrial health & industrial safety.
    Law
    I. Title II. Series
    344.104465

ISBN 0 273 03246 1

*The information in this book is intended as a general guide based upon the
legislation at the time of going to press. Neither the Bank, its staff or the author
can accept liability for any loss arising as a result of reliance upon any
information contained herein and readers are strongly advised to obtain
professional advice on an individual basis.*

Typeset, printed and bound in Great Britain

Contents

Preface

The Health and Safety at Work Act burst upon a suspecting world in 1974, alerted by its preceding Parliamentary Bill. Its importance has been well recognised but its contents and implications still need to be explained. Matters have been complicated by the ever-increasing regulations and codes of practice which it has generated. Concurrently, many areas of the older safety legislation have been repealed or revoked but what survives remains potently in force. No wonder the small firm is confused!

In response to this perceived need, this little book aims to bring a modicum of enlightenment in an acceptable way. Its limited compass inevitably means that much has had to be omitted; and the choice has not been easy but there is no one correct selection.

Small firms and the self-employed persons in business and the professions have been borne in mind in the presentation, and examples to illustrate points made have been picked with them primarily in mind. It is likely that the contents will interest others also for the 1974 Act involves everybody, directly or indirectly, now.

Alison Broadhurst
Autumn 1990

1 Why bother . . .?

Health and safety legislation applies to you □ Criminal safety law □ Common law □ How to get advice □ The scope of the subject □ Adopting a policy □ Planning and budgeting

Health and safety legislation applies to you

Modern health and safety legislation has its origins in a bill introduced in Parliament by Sir Robert Peel in 1802. This blossomed into the Health and Morals of Apprentices Act which became law in June of that year. The Act aimed at preventing the hardships imposed on the young generation and, in fact, also helped other workers by introducing some novel ideas like having to keep workplaces cleaner and providing windows for ventilation.

Since then, first the development of industry and then the massive flowering of technology in more recent times have led to a greater need for health and safety control. Providing safe[1] conditions is no longer a matter of commonsense, if ever it was. There are technicalities involved in apparently mundane risks, and hazards today may be invisible and not detectable by the senses (e.g. various forms of radiation).

The law has striven with varying success to keep up with the advancing use of plant and materials until the Health and Safety at Work Act 1974. This is a watershed act, dividing the old patchy law, albeit good of its kind, from the modern all-embracing kind which applies to all places of work, those who control them in any way and those who work there. It even applies to members of the public who are forbidden to interfere intentionally with anything provided under that act. It applies to you.

An inherent part

Health and safety are twin threads running through every business or professional enterprise. They are not optional extras to be added when you have time to spare. A new enterprise is not born with

---

[1] 'Safety' generally includes health in this book.

a silver spoon in its mouth but a copy of the Health and Safety at Work Act. Even so, safety has to be integrated with the other aspects of running the business, not hived off like some interesting but extraneous matter.

There is a lot of other legislation, too. Some of it is relevant to a wide range of premises, being of general application – like the Fire Precautions Act 1971, for instance. Some of it only applies to offices or shops or places of sport; but the bulk applies to factories and various other industrial activities which are notional factories (e.g. construction work). The Factories Act, in particular, has spawned a large family of regulations and the Health and Safety at Work Act emulates it by producing regulations and codes of practice. Some of these replace earlier sets of regulations, for example those relating to electricity, but others, like the classification, packaging and labelling of dangerous substances, venture into new territory. More are to come. Some, like these dangerous substances regulations, are affected by the European Community which seeks harmonization in due course among member countries.

This may all seem daunting but fortunately an individual firm will only be subject to those regulations which are specific to its activities. The regulations governing electricity will in practice be of universal application but those relating to lead or highly flammable liquids, for instance, will only be applicable where such materials are used or stored. The 1974 Act, as already stated, applies to all.

Criminal safety law

The Factories Act, the Health and Safety at Work Act and the others of this type which lay down the standards, together with their regulations, are part of the criminal law. In this respect, they are like income tax law or that relating to VAT. The pattern is similar. The legislation lays down the standards and the areas of their application. You have to carry out what Parliament has decided but if you fail, you are liable to be punished under the law. This usually means a fine but can lead to imprisonment in extreme cases.

Inspectors of the central government body, the Health and Safety Executive (HSE), and of local government (usually the Environmental Health Officers) enforce this law. Many, but not all, small firms (e.g. shops) will be inspected by the latter body. Their powers are outlined in Chapter 18 as are those of the HSE.

Common law

This, 'the basic law of the land', deals with the rights of persons who have been injured as a result of your negligence. Most claims under this heading are made by employees or ex-employees. However, the number of customers who make claims if, for instance, they fall while on your premises and are injured, is increasing.

Members of the public may also claim if they have been injured because of what they believe to be your negligence even if the accident occurred when not on your premises. This can happen, for instance, if you use a crane with the jib overhanging the street and it drops its load on a hapless pedestrian passing by.

You are liable in law for what your employees do in the course of their employment. If one is careless and causes injury to another employee – or anyone else – you will generally be liable. Today every employer must take out an insurance policy under the employer's liability law to cover claims which may be made against his or her firm by an injured employee. In practice, you may deem it wise to take additional cover for other accidents, too. Failure to insure for employer's liability attracts a very heavy financial penalty but you cannot insure against being prosecuted – this may happen for any breach of the criminal safety law.

Claims based on your alleged negligence, whether by an employee or anyone else, are part of the non-criminal, i.e. civil law.

How to get advice

To find out what requirements you have to fulfil, and how, you need advice. This should, of course, be authoritative. One important source is the inspector, whether of HSE or local government. Inspectors are required to advise as well as enforce.

Because of the many technicalities, there is a large and increasing array of official publications to help you. These range from detailed booklets to leaflets and pocket notes. The latter are designed for workpeople. Many leaflets and pocket notes are issued free by HSE and may be obtained as a result of a telephone call. Other publications are obtainable from HMSO usually at an ever-increasing cost which is presumably sufficient to keep them in the manner to which they seem to have become accustomed.

Official publications are generally practical and manage to avoid legal jargon in advising you what you should do. Last but, it is hoped, not least, this book seeks to advise and guide you as far as space permits.

The scope of the subject

The scope of the subject is wide but you need to identify which parts apply to your business. This will depend on what you do and how you do it. Small firms are especially vulnerable, for statistics show that they have a greater accident rate and suffer most if a key person is absent.

One small ceramics firm faced liquidation when unexpectedly high lead blood levels were found in their employees. Only the advice of the HSE and the firm's own cooperation saved their business.

All firms must have a safe system of work including a safe place of work, safe machinery, plant and equipment, and safety in the use of dangerous substances, handling, storage and methods of work as well as proper instruction, training and supervision – and management.

The place of work

Buildings as a whole and individual workshops, offices and other places have to be structurally sound and provided with adequate means of escape in case of fire. Inspectors have power to close down unsafe places without warning.

The working environment is important. Suitable heating, ventilation, lighting and freedom from harmful dusts, fumes, gases and excessive noise have to be ensured. Even outdoor sites may present hazards such as overhead high voltage power lines which may be accidentally contacted by, say, tipper lorries and cranes. If your employees have to work in the premises of others (including domestic premises), you still have a duty to protect them. For example, one firm's drivers had complained about unsafe means of access at bakeries where they delivered sacks of flour. To deal with the matter, the employers sent someone to check these and make suitable arrangements with the bakery firms.

Checklist

- Check the structural soundness of places at work
- Ensure fire safety
- Take precautions where there are low overhead power lines
- Prevent pollution of the workplace environment
- Deal with hazards in off-site places where your employees work

Machinery, plant and equipment

All dangerous parts of all machinery must be securely guarded. In most cases there are known standards, some of which are set out in regulations. Lifting plant such as cranes have an unnerving habit of falling over from time to time or dropping a load. All such plant and equipment have to be safely designed, constructed and maintained, and periodically examined by a competent person, usually an insurance company surveyor. His reports have to be kept available for inspection.

A safe electrical installation is essential for electricity is a killer. No unqualified person should be allowed to tamper with it. New machinery should comply with statutory standards but sometimes a machine slips through the net. Watch out for this. You will need to check second-hand equipment particularly carefully because it is your responsibility once you use any plant or machinery. Hired plant also needs to be checked by you. Beware of home-made contrivances. Improvisation is a fruitful source of danger.

In a furniture-restoring business a curious artefact was devised to flash off solvents from french polish. This was fashioned from a piece of timber and an unguarded electrical element. After one look the inspector issued a Prohibition ('stop') Notice.

Checklist

- Make sure that machinery is properly safeguarded
- Take proper precautions with lifting machinery
- Observe safety standards with pressurised plant
- Ensure safe electrical installations and maintenance

- Be especially careful about the safety of second-hand and hired machinery and plant
- Beware of improvisation

Dangerous substances

Review all substances which you use or store and check on their more unsavoury characteristics. Always use the safest material for any job. But if you do have to use dangerous substances, find out what precautions have to be taken. There are, for instance, flammables in various forms, solids, fumes, gases, dusts. Even loose paper lying on the floor in the packing department can burn nicely, given a sporting chance. Find out also about any regulations applying to the materials you have.

In one case liquefied petroleum (LP) gas escaped from a fuel tank believed to be empty. But as two employees walked out of the small factory the gas–air mixture exploded, demolishing the building, their jobs and probably the small firm itself.

Many materials are potentially dangerous to health when breathed (e.g. asbestos or lead), or when in contact with the skin (e.g. some solvents), and even a simple material like flour can cause dermatitis.

Checklist

- Use the safest materials possible
- Review safeguards for all substances stored or used
- Take care with flammable materials
- Ensure safe dealing with substances harmful to health

Handling and storage

We seem to be becoming a nation of bad backs. Not only do we undertake an excessive amount of manual handling but we do not train people enough in safe means of doing it. It is in the interests of productivity as well as safety that manhandling of goods should be minimised. Accidents happen not only from lifting excessive weights but as a result of unsafe methods.

A common fault is to underestimate the amount of space needed for handling and storage. This should be sufficient for dealing with raw materials and bought-in parts and components, work in progress, finished goods awaiting despatch or in temporary storage and those sudden deliveries which take up so much space. Some substances like petroleum can only be stored if you have the requisite licence. In some cases regulations may lay down the conditions under which you store materials such as LP gas. Waste products come in many guises and you will need to foresee what kind and amount of waste you will produce. Proper arrangements must be made for their disposal in accordance with current legislation. Some, like asbestos, must be disposed of only by approved means.

Checklist

- Reduce manual handling
- Ensure adequate storage space
- Obtain any necessary licences
- Ensure safe waste disposal

Adopting a policy

You are in control of the work and decide how it will be carried out. The methods you lay down need to be checked from time to time to ensure that your instructions are followed. Unsafe practices invite trouble.

In one small works leak testing of cylinders was done in an unsafe manner which also tended to deform the tanks being tested. An inspector, considering the method dangerous ordered the firm to introduce a safer method. To the firm's delight this also improved their productivity.

All this reviewing will show that a positive policy is needed. All but the tiniest of firms have to produce a written safety policy statement. Many matters require your decision from the start — for example, will employees be allowed to smoke at work? Sometimes

it is prohibited by law, like where there is an unusual fire risk or
where poisonous substances are used. Or, do you intend to employ
young persons under 18? If so are you prepared to give them the
extra attention that they need?

One firm allowed two young male employees to work alone at dangerous
woodworking machines contrary to regulations without adequate
supervision or training. The inevitable happened and one was injured.
He no doubt carries the scars to this day.

All employees in fact need training and instruction and to be
informed about the hazards and precautions of their work. But young
persons have to receive extra care in training.

Checklist

- Draw up your safety policy
- If required, embody this in a statutory policy statement
- Draw up safety rules – preferably in writing
- Remember that extra attention is needed for young persons
- Arrange instruction and training for all employees as necessary

Planning and budgeting

Planning for safety starts at Day One and continues afterwards. This
has to be reviewed from time to time and certainly when changes
are made, for instance, on the installation of new plant. Some cost
will be incurred if only for the keeping of records such as a
'Certificate of Means of Escape in Case of Fire'. All costs obviously
need to be budgeted for from the beginning. But not all safety matters
are costly – some even save money (e.g. by requiring new methods).

In planning, bear in mind that safety is more than just accident
prevention. That term means what it says, the prevention of
accidents. But if they do occur you need to have some plans for
dealing with them. This is the 'damage limitation' stage. Thus you
control flammables and sources of ignition to prevent fire breaking
out. But if it does break out you then need fire fighting and other
precautions. Both aspects have to figure in your planning – and

not just for fire of course. Today all persons have to be protected from danger arising from your activities wherever they are carried out. Employees, customers and other visitors, members of the general public (including trespassers) and the self-employed are under the protection of safety legislation now.

Checklist

1

- Plan and budget for safety
- Arrange for both accident prevention and damage limitation
- Remember everyone is protected

2 Factories, offices and shops

The importance of factory legislation □ How the Factories Act is being replaced □ What is a factory? □ Offices and shops □ Basic standards □ Checklist

The importance of factory legislation

Factories merit special mention, partly because they have been subject to safety legislation for such a long time and their special Act, the Factories Act 1961, was the major safety statute (outside the mining industry) prior to 1974. One consequence is that a lot of case law has built up which continues to be relevant. Indeed some points established have probably been settled for the long-term future. For instance, it has been laid down in the High Court that all persons working in a factory, whether employed by the occupier or not, are in most cases protected under the Act. This may be so even if at the time they are not doing the work they were employed to do.

Many cases have, not surprisingly, dealt with questions of machinery safety. The Act requires dangerous parts of machinery to be securely fenced, a matter which has been considered by the Courts on many occasions. This duty is an absolute one and allows of no exceptions even if the guarding is expensive, difficult or it interferes with the intended purpose of the machine. There has been some relaxation of this apparently harsh rule but only in certain, carefully identified circumstances. In effect, certain machines, such as some which cannot be used with secure fencing, are allowed to be used with a specific type of guarding which is less safe. Well-known examples are abrasive wheels and woodworking machines. A circular saw, for instance, must not be used unless the prescribed safeguards are provided to the requisite standard and are used properly. The relaxations are allowed only if the regulations say so.

Factory legislation includes many regulations as well as the 1961 Act and remains an important area of the law. But changes are taking place.

How the Factories Act is being replaced

This Act and its regulations will eventually be fully replaced by new legislation and the Health and Safety at Work Act. Meantime they coexist, but some quite large portions of the older law have already been replaced by the new. This piecemeal replacement produces a patchwork of legislation which is unavoidable. EC directives also influence this process.

Factory legislation remains very important for two reasons:

1.   It applies directly to factories, building operations and a number of other places.
2.   It sets a standard, sometimes in some detail, which is used in interpreting the newer legislation. All the new standards must be at least equal to the old and will often be more stringent.

The places to which it applies directly need therefore to be identified.

What is a factory?

The term 'factory' has a wider meaning than that of the dictionary. It obviously includes premises where articles are made. Also, by definition, it includes premises, even in the open air, carried on as a business, where at least one person is employed and in which:

● articles are altered (e.g. the alterations workroom of a dress shop)
● articles are repaired (e.g. a vehicle repair garage)
● articles are cleaned (e.g. a dry cleaning works)
● articles are broken up (e.g. a scrap metal works)
● articles are sorted incidentally to work in any factory (e.g. sorting waste paper for use at a factory elsewhere)
● articles are adapted for sale (e.g. ripening bananas by artificial heat)

Also included are such places as: abattoirs; a yard or dry dock where ships or vessels are constructed, repaired or refitted; premises where articles such as bottles or containers are washed or filled, or articles are packed incidentally to the purposes of any factory; laundries ancillary to another business (e.g. a hotel); printing works. Certain premises such as farms, mines and parts of quarries are excluded, being covered by other statutes.

Notional factories

In addition, some premises are expressly included as 'notional' factories. In particular, these include:

- electrical stations (e.g. for the purpose of an industrial or commercial undertaking)
- some charitable and reformatory institutions where articles are made or adapted for sale
- docks, wharfs and quays (including certain warehouses there)
- harbours or wet docks where constructing, repairing, refitting and breaking up a ship (as defined in merchant shipping legislation) are carried on
- certain other work on ships in harbour or wet dock (e.g. cleaning out oil/fuel tanks or bilges)
- building operations (see Chapter 4)
- works of engineering construction (see Chapter 4)

   Comprehensive though it is, this list of premises subject to the Factories Act is not complete but it indicates the more common kinds of small businesses. A factory may be any size, even a single room or part of one. You should make enquiries if you are in any doubt as you have to notify the inspector in writing before opening a factory. Also within seven days of starting a building operation which is expected to last at least six weeks you must send in a written notification.

Offices and shops

The Offices, Shops and Railway Premises Act 1963 is modelled on the Factories Act but has a lesser technical content. An office is a building (or part) where administration, writing, book-keeping, sorting papers, filing, typing, duplicating, machine calculating, drawing, the editorial preparation of matter for publication, handling money, telephone and telegraph operating is carried on and someone is employed. As in the factory legislation, the purpose is to protect the employees. All offices and shops are also subject to the Health and Safety at Work Act. A 'shop' has its ordinary meaning and extends to other places used for retail trade or business, and to wholesale warehouses (except docks warehouses listed as factories – see above). 'Retail trade or business' includes catering establishments open to the public, retail auction sales and libraries for lending books and periodicals.

Basic standards

In so far as similar plant and equipment is used, the safety standards for factories and offices are similar. Examples are those relating to lifts and hoists, fork-lift trucks, belt conveyors, compactors as used in industry and, for example, in hotels and restaurants. Environmental standards are similar too (e.g. for cleanliness, heating and ventilation).

Checklist

- Do not overlook factory legislation
- Many kinds of premises are classed as factories
- There is a special legislation for offices and shops

3 Moving to new premises?

Is there enough space? □ Stairways □ Lifts and hoists □ Floor loadings □ Fire precautions □ Heating and ventilation □ Washing and toilet facilities □ The general rule □ Checklist

Is there enough space?

In addition to checking for general soundness premises which you intend to occupy, there are some pitfalls to avoid. You may be satisfied that there is adequate room for your plant, furniture and employees, but what about the things you have to store? Is there sufficient space, especially after a new delivery? If you use flammable liquids, is there a suitable safe store? If your business prospers, you may need more space for people and goods perhaps – is there room for expansion? What about vehicles delivering goods to you – is there a yard? If not, how will you handle them? Surely you cannot leave them on the pavement. If there is a yard, is there turning room for vehicles? If not, you may need to supply an assistant to help drivers to back out – blind reversing causes many accidents. You will no doubt check car parking facilities too.

Stairways

Are the stairways in good condition, fitted with handrails and well lighted? Check the light switches for staircase lights. Sometimes they are such that employees have to grope up or down in the dark until reaching a switch. Make sure that no doors open directly on to stairs. Remember that you and your staff are likely to have to carry things up or down at times. Spiral staircases are often unsuitable.

Lifts and hoists

Perhaps there is a lift for passengers and goods. If so, confirm that the landlord has it properly examined and maintained, if the premises are shared with others. Otherwise you may be responsible. Is there a hoist for goods? And if so, is it suitable for the things you handle? Regular examination and maintenance are essential.

A small firm had a laboratory located on the top floor of a three-storey building. They overlooked the need for a lift and employees had to carry full gas cylinders up. On occasion, one man would do this alone and he was found dragging a cylinder upstairs and banging it on every step as he did so. This was very dangerous.

Floor loadings

If you have plant of any kind which imposes a heavy load on the floor, check the safe floor loading of any upper floor where you propose to install it. A fork-lift truck, for instance, is for ground floor and outdoor use as it imposes too heavy a concentrated load for an upper floor. Even in new workshops, problems may arise.

A new annexe attached to a factory building had cable ducts made in the floor which had been covered over with concrete slabs about 300 mm (12 in) square and 25 mm (1 in) thick. They had no steel reinforcement, having been installed for light workshop traffic. When machinery was being installed, a portable gantry mounted on four wheels was used to move some of the machine parts. Whilst in use, some of the concrete cover slabs fractured under one of its wheels. This caused the gantry to tilt and trap one of the men pushing it. Calculations revealed that the load on this wheel was nearly half a ton which was too heavy a concentrated load for the floor.

Fire precautions

Fire precautions are obviously of extreme importance and you will need to clarify who is responsible for what if you share a building. Some, at least, of the responsibility rests on you. Means of detecting fire, sounding the alarm, fire fighting and means of escape for everyone in the building need attention. (See Chapter 7.)

Heating and ventilation

Heating and ventilation are central to the health and comfort of the working environment. If you are going to use the top floor of a building for sedentary work, there may be problems of low temperature, at least on cold Monday mornings. After being unheated over the weekend, this is a testing time. If you share a building, check how much control you have over the heating system. Check also, where appropriate, the arrangements to prevent Legionnaire's disease. (See Chapter 6.)

3

Washing and toilet facilities

Washing and toilet facilities are often shared where there are two or more tenants. Check that there is sufficient provision for everyone and ascertain whether the landlord accepts responsibility for cleaning and maintenance. (See Chapter 5.)

The general rule

The general rule in shared occupancy of buildings is that the landlord deals with those parts of the premises used by two or more tenants whilst the individual firm is responsible for its own part. The contract should be checked on the matter before you sign.

Checklist

- Is there enough space?
- Are the stairways safe?
- Check that lifts and hoists are maintained
- Beware of excessive floor loading
- Check the fire precautions
- Are the washing and toilet facilities adequate?
- Clarify the division (if any) of responsibilities

4 Building sites and other workplaces

Construction work □ Main causes of accidents □ Accident prevention □ Site planning □ Checklist □ Other workplaces □ Checklist

Construction work

This has a distressing safety record in which small firms, sadly, play a prominent part. Construction work includes building operations and works of engineering construction.

Building operations

The term 'building operation' includes not only the construction of buildings but also their structural alteration, repair, maintenance (including repainting, redecoration and external cleaning of a structure), demolition and preparation for and laying of the foundation.

Works of engineering construction

The term 'works of engineering construction' includes: the construction of any railway line or siding except one upon an existing railway; the construction, structural alteration, repair or demolition of any dock, harbour, inland navigation, tunnel, bridge, viaduct, waterworks, reservoir, pipeline, aqueduct, sewer, sewage works, gasholder, steel or reinforced concrete structure (other than a building), road, airfield, sea defence works, river works, other similar civil engineering works, pipeline for conveyance of anything except water. There are some exceptions with regard to work upon a railway or tramway.

Main causes of accidents

Fatalities and serious injuries arise especially because of people

- falling from a height (e.g. scaffolding)
- being struck by a moving vehicle
- being trapped by something collapsing or overturning (e.g. a dumper)
- being struck by various other moving objects (e.g. falling loads)

Serious injuries are also regularly recorded as being caused by

- handling, lifting and carrying things
- slips, trips and falls on the same level
- being struck against something
- contact with machinery or material being operated on by machine (e.g. concrete mixers)
- exposure to or contact with harmful substances
- electricity (although a high percentage may be fatal)

Accident prevention

Falling people characterise the industry as they tumble off roofs, scaffolding, ladders and other places. A clue to safeguarding is the figure of 2 metres (6 ft 6 in). Whenever there is a risk of falling further than this, the fullest precautions are needed.

Roof work

Roof work produces a regular quota of accidents often involving serious injuries. Workpeople fall off the edges of roofs and through fragile ones like asbestos roofs.

A partner in a firm of general builders fell 3.4 m (11 ft) through the asbestos cement roof of a factory. He was carrying out minor repairs working on his own, before falling to his death. A single plank 228 mm (9 in) wide was found at the approaches to the roof.

Before requiring anyone to work on a roof consider whether the work could be done in another, safer way. Could the job be carried out from underneath, standing on a platform, for example? There are strict regulations requiring the use of crawling boards or ladders with barriers to prevent anyone falling off the edge. Other precautions may be needed too, dependent on the circumstances.

Scaffolding

There are various types of scaffolding but all have to be well constructed, stable and suitably secured against collapse. Only experienced persons should be allowed to erect scaffolds and there are specialist firms available. The walkways should be kept clear of obstructions and free from slippery surfaces. Care is needed to prevent overloading. Guard rails and toe boards or equivalent guarding is needed and proper access has to be provided. Scaffolds should be inspected before being used for the first time, after any alteration or following severe weather. Regular examinations at weekly intervals by a competent person are also required and the results must be entered in a register kept for the purpose. This is Form 91, Part 1, obtainable from the HMSO.

Tower scaffolds are often used by painters and others who do lighter work requiring movement from place to place. They should be obtained from a reputable supplier, safe design and construction being important. There are restrictions on the height-to-base ratio so that the centre of gravity is not too high, causing instability. The working platform should be closely boarded with boards of adequate thickness. Guard rails and toe boards have to be provided on all sides of the working platform.

An electrician and his mate were installing trunking beneath a ceiling. They were using a mobile scaffold tower made from lightweight metal scaffolding. The working platform was about 3 m (10 ft) above ground level and the tower itself was about 2.1 m (7 ft) long and about 0.9 m (3 ft) wide. Instead of climbing up on the inside of the short side, the electrician began to climb up outside the long side, using the cross members as a foothold. To make matters worse, his mate did not wait but began to climb up at the same time, following the electrician. This was enough to cause the scaffold to overturn so that both men were injured.

Ladders

Every ladder and folding stepladder must be of good construction, of suitable and sound material and of adequate strength for the purpose for which it is used. Its proper maintenance is important. Timber ladders must never be painted − this hides defects.

For safety purposes, ladders are divided into three classes. Class 1 is suitable for construction work where the ladder is in frequent use and subject to substantial loads. Class 2 is intended for lighter trades such as decorating, where relatively low loads are involved and use is less frequent. Class 3 is for light use (e.g. domestic purposes).

A self-employed roofing contractor carrying a batch of roofing tiles fell to his death from about 4.5 m (15 ft) off a two-stage timber extension ladder fitted with aluminium rungs. The ladder, which was some three years old, failed when both stiles snapped near the base of the upper section. The HSE investigated the accident and said that the ladder may have been overloaded. A Class 1 ladder should have been used instead of the Class 2 one which the roofer had employed.

In use, ladders should be erected on a firm, level base and non-slip sleeves or similar may be needed if, for example, the floor is slippery. The head of the ladder should rest on a firm, solid surface. The '1 in 4' rule should be observed, that is the slope should be such that the foot of the ladder is one metre out for every four metres of height. Ladders should be securely lashed near the top against displacement, or other adequate means should be used where top lashing is not possible. Having a second person to 'foot' the ladder is only effective for short ladders.

Do not use metal ladders or timber ladders with metal reinforcement where there is a risk of electrical contact (with live conductors). All ladders should extend at least 1.05 m (3 ft 6 in) above the place of landing. All ladders should be regularly inspected for such defects as splits, warping, worn or missing rungs, damaged feet and the like. Defective ladders should be taken out of use for repair or scrapped. They should not be consigned to a pile of rubbish for disposal but removed entirely, otherwise someone will come along and pick them up and use them.

Excavations

Accidents caused by the collapse of excavations are usually serious and sometimes fatal. They are often caused by inadequate support. Other matters to avoid are placing materials and moving plant too close to the edge. The sides of large, open excavations should be battered where appropriate. All should be inspected daily and thoroughly examined every seven days. A record of these examinations should be kept in the official register (i.e. Form 91, Part 1, Section B).

Weather

A subject of importance to all who work outside is the weather. Bad weather can quickly convert a safe site into a dangerous one in minutes. Walkways can suddenly become treacherously slippery, the sides of untimbered trenches can be loosened dangerously and this could lead to collapse. High winds wreak their own kind of havoc, blowing things over, and can present a nasty hazard to anyone carrying a sheet of material.

Demolition

You need a properly experienced person to supervise demolition work and if there is another contractor on the site it is necessary to consult him as regards, say, methods and timing of the work. This applies equally to those who are self-employed.

As a preliminary, attention has to be paid to any risks in connection with services such as water, gas and electricity. Risks of flooding, explosive accumulations of gas, electrocution or striking underground cables have all to be taken seriously. Every necessary precaution against unplanned collapse must obviously be taken.

A number of two-storey cottages, which were 70 years old, were being demolished. They formed a terrace of five, but three of them had already been partly demolished. This earlier work had left a 110 mm (4.5 in) wall which was 6.4 m (21 ft) long and 7.3 m (24 ft) high, standing. At the extreme ends of the wall were two short portions of 230 mm (9 in) brickwork – the remains of the front and rear walls. The contractor planned to weaken the wall so that the workmen could push it over manually. This never happened because the wall collapsed whilst being weakened and a workman was killed. The accident could have been prevented if the wall had been shored against collapse and demolition carried on piecemeal. The person in charge had failed to appreciate how dangerous the wall was.

Site planning

Preliminary work includes notifying the HSE on Form 10 that construction work is starting (unless it is expected to be completed in less than six weeks) and any necessary contact with competent bodies (e.g. with the electricity authority to locate existing services and, where necessary, to isolate overhead supplies).

Ensure that statutory forms such as registers are available as well as any company documents. Discuss, where necessary, your safety policy with that of other contractors on site and exchange safety policy documents if appropriate. Plan the health and welfare facilities whether shared with others or not. These include suitable arrangements for taking meals, drinking water, washing and toilet facilities, clothing accommodation and first aid. Check whether there is a telephone available in case of emergency. It is good routine practice to post up details of the arrangements for summoning an ambulance. If no telephone is available, ensure that transport is always available in case of need.

If you intend to use highly flammable materials (e.g. LP gas), make proper arrangements for storage and use. Where special fire precautions are needed, as when working in or on a large building, check these beforehand and inform your employees.

On one small building site there was a small mess hut provided with a gas ring and a gas oven, each with its own cylinder of LP gas. The kettle was heating merrily on the gas ring but as meal time approached it was found necessary to replace the gas cylinder for the oven. One man therefore fetched a full cylinder whilst another man removed the almost empty one. Unfortunately, this man turned the control 'on' instead of 'off'. Mercifully, no one was seriously hurt but the resulting explosion destroyed the hut.

Checklist

- Construction sites also include places where work such as demolition or repairs is undertaken

- Accidents in the industry are too many and often very serious
- Watch out for the 'two-metre' standard generally
- Falls can often be prevented
- Fragile or sloping roofs present special dangers
- Use only safe scaffolding – and examine it regularly
- Ensure that ladders are sound and properly used
- Keep workpeople out of unsafe excavations
- Watch for sudden hazards in bad weather
- Ensure that demolition work is properly supervised
- Carry out proper site planning
- Protect members of the public from harm

Other workplaces

All places have their particular health and safety problems and share
with others many of the commoner ones. A few examples of some
of the special features for a number of different kinds of workplaces
illustrate this.

Catering establishments

Kitchen equipment can be quite dangerous mechanically and some
machines (e.g. vegetable slicing machines and power-operated meat
mincers) are designated as specially dangerous. There is a risk of
fire from oil, especially when being heated. Grease which collects
in ventilation ducts will tend to spread any fire which occurs.

Shops

If flammable or explosive materials such as LP gas or fireworks are
stored on the premises, special precautions are needed. Pharmacies,
for instance, may have many gas cylinders and special care should
be taken. And beware of leaving loose packing material lying about:
it can be a fire risk. Sometimes a lot of manual handling of fairly
heavy or difficult loads is done and proper lifting techniques are
required. Check also on means of access for employees about the
premises, including reaching up to high shelves.

Sports and leisure centres

Among the safety problems are those relating to the fact that members of the public as well as staff will be on the premises. Ensure that access to gymnasium equipment is available only to adults and that adequate supervision is provided. For wet places like the surrounds of swimming pools and even the showers, take precautions against persons slipping especially as their feet may be bare. Have safe surfaces, beware of sudden changes of surfaces or hidden steps, and clean and drain the showers so that there is not a build-up of slippery material there.

Caravan parks

The road system should be planned for safety and if you have shower baths in a separate building, observe precautions to prevent people slipping. Also, arrange for an emergency alarm in the shower block to summon help in case of accident. First aid provision should take account of the number of people on the site.

Nursing homes

The lifting and carrying of patients is demanding, so nurses and others who do this work need to be adequately trained. The amount of lifting and carrying should in any case be minimised, for example by the layout, so as to limit the distances involved. Wherever possible, mechanical lifting aids should be provided, ranging from individual personal slinging devices to lifts.

Educational establishments

In some establishments there are laboratories with dangerous materials but in all there are likely to be chemicals for cleaning purposes. The manufacturer's recommendations should always be followed carefully. Cleaners should be provided with gloves and other protective wear as necessary and be made to wear them. In laboratories they will need to take special care with waste bins which may contain contaminated material and glassware. The safe disposal of all waste is a matter for the management to arrange.

School caretakers, for example, can be exposed to high concentrations of fumes when removing clinker and ash from solid fuel boilers. Advice should be sought from boiler manufacturers or solid fuel promotion bodies. Lecturers, students and others may use or store, and not only in laboratories, highly flammable liquids. The list includes a host of solvents, paints, thinners, adhesives, cleaning liquids and reprographic fluids. Be aware of what is being stored and used, and ensure precautions are taken. The basic rule remains: use the safest material for any job and in the minimum amount. Chemicals should never be put into milk bottles, jam jars or other unsuitable and unlabelled containers. It is a recipe for disaster to someone one day. Don't do it.

Sometimes there is a security problem, for instance with language schools where there is a constantly changing student population. It may be deemed useful to have doors locked against unauthorised entry. In all cases, make sure that everyone is able to get out in case of fire and that all doors are capable of being opened easily from the inside.

Farms

The dangers pertinent to farms and the safeguards required would need a whole book to outline. Here only a few points can be identified although what is said in all chapters is of relevance to farms.

Agriculture which includes not only farming but also horticulture and forestry is a major industry with its own special problems as well as those shared by other commercial undertakings. One special feature is the presence of children, although parents should prevent their offspring from trespassing into areas of risk. As there are dangerous machines and toxic substances like pesticides, special care is obviously necessary.

Safety is important on fish farms. The construction and maintenance of the installations, the provision of guard rails, foot rails, safe working surfaces, vehicle ways, and various means of rescue are among a number of essential safeguards. Diving regulations apply to diving operations both inside and outside cages. (These also apply to divers in other places of work.) Life jackets should be provided and worn at fish farms and at such places as oyster beds and areas where boats are hired out to the public either for fishing or for recreational activities.

Checklist

- Safeguard dangerous machinery and provide adequate fire precautions in catering establishments
- In shops take special care with dangerous materials and manual handling

- Provide safe access for visitors to leisure establishments and protect them as necessary
- Plan road systems and emergency alarms in caravan parks
- Provide lifting aids wherever possible in nursing homes
- Watch out for the special risks of educational establishments

5 What facilities should be provided?

Washing facilities □ Sanitary accommodation □ Messrooms □ Clothing accommodation □ First aid □ Seating □ Checklist

Basic facilities for health and safety are required for all employees in every firm. The main ones are:

- washing facilities and sanitary accommodation
- messroom or similar arrangements
- clothing accommodation
- first aid
- seating
- protective wear

5

They have to be provided by you.

Washing facilities

These should include wash-basins with warm and cold water laid on, soap and clean towels (or the equivalent). The working standard is usually a minimum of one basin for 20 or fewer employees. If there are extra hygienic requirements or there is a special risk to the skin (as in bakeries), one basin per ten employees is needed. If there is a health risk such as lead, one basin per five workers is the minimum.

Where facilities are shared, for instance in office blocks, make sure that these minimum standards are met. When the washing facilities are part of a toilet area, these minimum numbers of basins must be met for men and women separately. If you employ one man and one woman you would then need two wash-basins.

Sanitary accommodation

Separate provision must usually be made for men and women. The general standard is one convenience for up to 25 female employees

plus one for up to 25 male employees. The facilities should be
partitioned off so as to secure privacy and there should be an
intervening ventilated space between the accommodation and
workroom.

Sanitary accommodation should be provided on a building site
on the same scale.

Messrooms

Canteens are not essential for small firms but some arrangements
for meal breaks – with or without food, or facilities for heating
it or for boiling water – represent good practice. Some quite small
firms allot a room for the purpose and often provide tea-making
facilities there. Tea- and coffee-making machines about the premises
are sometimes preferred. If toxic substances such as lead are used,
separate accommodation for taking food and drink is necessary.
If LP gas cylinders are used for heating gas rings or ovens, take care
to ensure that they are carefully handled. (See Chapter 7.)

Clothing accommodation

This is required under two headings:

- outdoor clothing
- protective clothing

Provision should be made for outdoor clothing during working hours.
This must be secure, especially against theft, and means of drying
should be provided. A hot pipe running beneath a row of lockers
may be suitable. If you use a portable electric fire, care is needed
to prevent fire and the appliance should not be placed too close
to the clothing.

Accommodation for protective clothing – and items such as
footwear, safety helmets and gloves also – is necessary. What has
to be provided obviously depends on the nature of the item: for
work with lead, for instance, adequate changing and storage facilities
are needed.

First aid

Generally, only simple facilities are needed unless some special risk
arises. In practice, if people other than your employees regularly

come on to your premises, you should bear them in mind when deciding what to provide. This applies to customers in a shop or students in a school, for instance. The main points to consider are:

- the number of first aid boxes to be provided
- their location
- their contents
- qualified first-aiders
- outside help available

You have to make adequate and suitable provision for your particular circumstances. You therefore need to review your premises and activities to assess what your needs are. What you provide should be tailor-made by you for your firm.

For most small compact establishments a single box may be enough but more may be needed if your employees are dispersed over a wide area. A box should be readily accessible to everyone, so it should be suitably located. If your employees work alone or in isolated locations (e.g. on farms), you should provide small travelling kits. If your employees work on a building site together with others, you should agree with the main contractor about the provision of first aid. Put that agreement in writing and satisfy yourself that adequate provision is in fact made.

Each first-aid box should contain standard items including adhesive and other dressings, a triangular bandage, at least one sterile eye pad, and a guidance card or leaflet giving first-aid advice. If in doubt seek advice from EMAS (see p. 60). A qualified first-aider is always an asset, although it is not compulsory for small firms to have one, and it is wise to encourage members of staff to be trained in first aid. In some firms, a financial inducement is offered.

Consider from the beginning what outside help (i.e. hospitals and doctors) is available locally. Post emergency telephone numbers up by the telephone in case of need. If there are no such facilities locally, increase your on-the-spot provision, and don't forget to check the first-aid boxes regularly!

Seating

This has to be considered under two headings:

- seats for regular use by employees who do their work seated (e.g. at a conveyor).

All too often seats are not suitable for the particular operations; for instance, it is known that some of the stress felt by VDU operators may be traced back to unsuitable seating.

● seats for occasional use, such as those provided for shop assistants to use when they are not serving customers.

Checklist

● Provide suitable washing facilities
● Provide suitable sanitary accommodation
● Provide somewhere for eating food
● Provide clothing accommodation
● Provide first-aid boxes
● Ensure medical help is available
● Provide suitable seats

6 The working environment

What is a suitable temperature? □ What is good ventilation? □ Lighting standards □ Noise □ Vibration □ Good housekeeping □ Checklist

People work best if they are reasonably comfortable at work. This depends largely on temperature, humidity, ventilation, lighting, noise and other characteristics of the physical environment. For most working environments, you have a large measure of control and penny-pinching on such matters is a false economy.

You and your employees spend a significant part of your life in the working environment which you provide. Each has his or her individual 'microclimate' which affects health and well-being. Those near heaters or windows may have different immediate environments than others; some are more sensitive to heat, cold, draughts and so on; some like working alone, others do not.

A firm was about to move premises and consulted its employees (it even took them over the new premises before the move). Most seemed quite happy about the arrangements, but the telephone operator was very unhappy. She was moving from a position where other people constantly passed by – with all the social contacts that implied – to a basement office which, no matter how pleasant, was off the beaten track for other members of the staff. She quite reasonably saw herself cut off and isolated; rather than face this prospect, she handed in her notice.

If you propose to install an open-plan office, bear this kind of thing in mind. Not everyone will appreciate its communal aspects and may feel under constant surveillance and miss the privacy which a small office or room provides. There are pros and cons to weigh up before making the decision. One aspect which is often overlooked is that fire spreads more easily in large unbroken spaces because barriers to fire spread are absent; even if partitions are used they are not enough to hold back a fire which breaks out.

What is a suitable temperature?

The ideal temperature depends upon the nature of the work. Many years ago a minimum standard of 15.5°C (60°F) was set for sedentary work; today, that is regarded as too low. A guide to suitable ranges of temperatures is:

- sedentary work: 19 – 21°C (65 – 70°C)
- light work: 15.5 – 19.0°C (60 – 65°F)
- heavy work: 13 – 15.5°C (55 – 60°F)

In some situations you have little or no control over the ambient temperature (e.g. work at ovens, furnaces and other hot plant; work inside cold stores and other cold places; outdoor work). For hot environments, do all you can to improve conditions by insulation, additional local ventilation or other means. Then – and for cold conditions – do what you can for the individual. Sometimes this means, for instance, that you have to provide insulating clothing and to arrange for extra work pauses. Weather protection by suitable clothing and huts or other shelter is generally needed for outdoor workers. Excessive humidity, especially if associated with a high temperature, is to be avoided.

What is good ventilation?

Fresh air is required for several reasons:

- for respiration
- to dilute airborne impurities like body odour, tobacco smoke (if permitted in the workplace), etc.
- to remove excess heat
- to dilute dusts, fumes and other process impurities

Adequate air movement is needed to provide a feeling of freshness without causing disagreeable draughts. Fresh air is distinguished from recirculated air such as is found in air-conditioning systems. These allow some impurities to build up which on occasion reach an unacceptable level.

Sick building syndrome

Minor illnesses like headaches and eye trouble are known to affect people working in modern, well-sealed buildings with mechanical ventilation or air conditioning compared with workers in older, naturally ventilated ones. This is known as 'sick building syndrome' and its causes have not yet been fully identified.

Legionnaire's disease

This was first identified in 1976 and appears as a form of pneumonia. The cause is a bacterium which is found in many recirculating and hot water systems such as those installed in large office blocks. Most outbreaks of the disease have been associated with hot water services and recirculating cooling water systems of air conditioning plant. These systems are often of poor design or badly maintained. Prevention is largely a technical matter and if you have an office in a large block, check with the owners that the maintenance, cleaning, testing and operating procedures are adequate.

Advice may be sought from the Medical Officer for Environmental Health of the local authority or the director of the local public health laboratory. Any outbreak in England and Wales should be reported to the Medical Officer of Health of the local authority or, in Scotland, to the Community Medicine Specialist and the HSE or Environmental Health Department of the local authority.

Humidifier fever

This illness is not the same as Legionnaire's disease, although both arise from the same source, i.e. contaminated water systems in buildings. It is a flu-like condition caused by the inhalation of fine droplets of water from humidifiers which have become contaminated. An example comes from the print industry where humidifiers are used to stabilise paper size and condition.

Prevention is by:

● choosing a suitable humidifier system (e.g. steam humidifier);
● maintaining it free from contamination by inspecting it weekly and taking care of its cleanliness.

If, in spite of your precautions, you have a problem, turn off the humidifier, notify a doctor and call in a ventilation specialist.

Lighting standards

Adequate and suitable lighting is needed:

- to enable people to see what they are doing and where they are going
- to illuminate potential hazards such as a hidden step
- to foster cleanliness
- to prevent eye strain

Standards have risen over the years and there is no excuse today for inadequate illumination. To be suitable, it should for instance also be free from glare, pools of darkness should be excluded, fluorescent lighting should not flicker, and excessive and sudden contrast should be avoided. To get the best out of your lighting system, keep light fittings clean and have a light-coloured ceiling to reflect the light.

An office worker left a brilliantly lighted building one winter afternoon. As he did so and stepped into the poorly lighted yard where there were deep shadows, he was blinded for the moment, tripped over a low, flat truck, fell and fractured his skull.

Noise

Measuring noise is a technical matter and the practical approach is first to decide whether you have a noise problem. If so, try and exclude, or at least reduce it, at source. Quieter machines are desirable and if you are purchasing plant, consider how much noise in use it produces. You could be buying a noise problem also, with the duty of dealing with it.

Having minimised the noise created, the next step is to contain it as far as possible by insulation of some kind. A common example of containment − partial, at least − is covering a noisy computer printer. Then you consider the need for ear protection for individuals who are exposed to excessive noise. In some very noisy environments and where little can be done in practice to reduce the noise to acceptable levels, you may need to designate an area as an 'Ear Protection Zone'. This should be so marked, unauthorised personnel kept out and suitable ear protection provided for those allowed to enter.

Noise problems have been the subject of a lot of discussion and research in recent years. The public has become more critical of noise imposed by the environment, whether from pneumatic drills, road traffic or a host of industrial noises emanating from factories and other places of work. Noise has also become important to people because they no longer accept that hearing loss is an inevitable result of working in a noisy environment. Protection is demanded.

Our ears can respond to a remarkably wide range of sound levels and practical sound measurements are made on a logarithmic scale and counted in decibels. Noise can damage the ears by:

- very loud noises such as explosions which can rupture ear drums;
- prolonged exposure to less intense noise which can cause irreversible damage.

In the latter case, the damage increases with the loudness of the noise and the length of exposure to it. If it is so noisy at work, even in parts only, that you have to shout to carry on a conversation, you almost certainly have a noise problem. This applies to individual machines too. In such cases action is needed, and you must:

- identify any areas of high noise levels where people work;
- in these areas comply with the best practice on noise, on which you will generally need expert advice;
- be on your guard for new noises (e.g. because of poorly maintained machines).

Vibration

The hazards of vibration are widely overlooked and it may be difficult to find out much about it. Yet it is a real problem and the effects can be very harmful. Several types of injury or disease may be caused by prolonged exposure to high levels of local vibration. The best known one is Vibration White Finger (VWF), but there are others too. In some countries there is a condition known as 'vibration disease' which is described with reference to a wide range of bodily effects. Tools associated with VWF include pneumatic hammers and other machines, hand-held portable grinders, chain saws and electrically-driven vibrating tools generally. Regular use of any of these may cause finger, hand and arm problems, in particular. Other effects have been recorded also. Seek expert help if you have a problem.

A man employed as gardener-handyman at a country house had to use a chain saw from time to time. For months he would not have to handle it then he might have to do so for several days running. After only 18 months' employment – and he was aged in his early thirties – he noticed that his hands felt numb and cold. He consulted a doctor who diagnosed VWF.

Stress

There are also the non-physical aspects of the working environment which are relevant to health and safety. For instance, stress is now recognised as having an important influence on people in all kinds of jobs and at all levels. The context in which people work may have a significant effect. Stress may be caused, for instance, by:

- the nature of the work (e.g. pressure of conveyor-belt working);
- the pace of working (e.g. to reach set targets);
- payment systems (e.g. incentive systems may lead to 'corner-cutting' in safety);
- repetition and monotony;
- shift work;
- the attitude of supervisors and managers (and perhaps yours);
- the behaviour of other employees.

It is wise to bear such matters in mind for not everyone responds in the same way and stressed employees present a problem.

Good housekeeping

This homely term has relevance in every workplace. It means cleanliness, tidiness and maintenance of the environment free from unnecessary risk. It is also an important fire precaution (see Chapter 7). Regular cleaning is an obvious need as is periodical redecoration – with extra careful hygiene where food is handled. It is necessary to keep premises free from such unwelcome visitors as cockroaches, not to mention rats and mice. Whilst floors are wet during cleaning, keep people away and put up a warning notice 'wet floor'. Avoid having trailing cables where people have to walk. Remove broken glass promptly. Even cabbage leaves left lying on the floor have caused workpeople to slip and get hurt. Interior walls, partitions, ceilings and other parts of the structure of a building have not only to be kept clean but redecorated periodically, unless tiled. The frequency depends partly on the processes carried on, because some cause more rapid deterioration of the surface than others, and partly on the kind of paint or surface covering applied. Records of redecoration should be kept for inspection.

Window cleaning

Window cleaning is needed regularly. You should be aware of the means of access to all windows. Roof windows, for example, may be awkward to reach and this could create safety problems. Windows in fragile roofs present a special danger and asbestos roofs are deceptively fragile to walk or even stand on. For flat roofs, lightweight staging should be provided unless permanent walkways are installed. On sloping roofs well-secured roof ladders or crawling boards are needed. It must be faced that the precautions may increase the cost somewhat but safety is important. If you employ an outside firm of window cleaners make sure that you have done all you should to provide safe conditions for them and remind them of the need to work safely – you are paying them to do so.

6

Checklist

- Provide a suitable temperature
- Improve conditions at hot and cold processes as far as possible
- Provide protective clothing as necessary
- Ventilate by suitable means
- Check for minor illnesses in air-conditioned rooms
- Ensure the proper maintenance of air-conditioning systems
- Provide adequate and suitable lighting
- Minimise the noise in the workplace
- Be aware of vibration risks
- Provide ear protection if necessary
- Practise good housekeeping

7 Fire precautions and security

Fire as a serious danger □ What are the possible sources of ignition? □ What is fuel for a fire? □ Is fire detection apparatus necessary? □ What about fire fighting? □ Is security relevant? □ Checklist

Fire as a serious danger

Fires benefit nobody and can put you out of business temporarily – or permanently. They even gobble up your business papers and records. They obviously damage property and unfortunately sometimes lead to serious, even fatal, injuries. Your first objective is to prevent it happening; but you also need to consider how to deal with a fire – before it happens. A fire needs:

- a source of ignition to start it;
- a fuel to start and sustain it;
- oxygen to support combustion;
- sufficient temperature to keep it going.

All these factors are present in indoor places of work and often outdoors. They provide the clues to fire precautions generally.

What are the possible sources of ignition?

Common ones are:

- electricity
- smouldering cigarette ends
- open flames
- matches
- heaters

Electric installations should be suitable for the work; for example, for some processes, flameproof equipment is needed. All repairs and modifications to the system should be done by a qualified electrician. In due course, the complete installation will need to be replaced so have it tested periodically.

It is up to you, usually, whether to allow cigarette smoking on the premises. If you do, you will need to control it by confining it to certain areas and times. But this still allows a potential source of ignition to be present which you could avoid. In some cases, as where highly flammable or radioactive substances are used, smoking is prohibited.

Open flames from gas burners and welding apparatus are examples of common ignition sources (sparks from welding should be included also). Matches which are thrown away at the workplace may be still alight, thus creating a further hazard. Electric radiant heaters too can cause fires to start.

In one small factory, a radiant heater was placed in the cloakroom to dry the employees' clothing which was wet. The heat dried the nearest clothing, the localised temperature then rose and suddenly some overheated clothing burst into flame. The factory was badly damaged.

What is fuel for a fire?

Almost anything will burn if the temperature is high enough. Fires start with any material which acts as tinder when ignited. Highly flammable materials are legion. Examples are:

- liquids such as solvents and oils;
- solids such as loose paper and polyurethane foam;
- fumes and gases such as acetylene and LP gas.

The first rule is to use the safest materials that you can, then to have the minimum amount on the premises which enables work to proceed. The bulk should be stored away from the building in a suitable place. For the storage of petroleum and certain petroleum products, a licence to store is needed from the local authority. Post a clear warning notice outside the store. In the workroom, keep the main supplies in a metal cupboard or bin, duly labelled on the outside. Use safety containers at the process, if possible, and control any spillage by doing the work over a tray.

Good housekeeping should ensure that loose paper, cardboard, plastics and other flammables do not lie about. Be aware of less obvious risks such as hydrogen gas, which is flammable and is given off from battery charging (e.g. for your fork-lift truck). Another matter often overlooked is that a so-called 'empty' drum which has contained a flammable liquid is still quite dangerous. Do not apply heat to it and dispose of it safely.

Gas cylinders

Many cylinders contain flammable gas (e.g. LP gas) and need to be stored, handled and used with care. Never store cylinders of heavy gas below ground level as any escaping gas lying about can creep into places thus presenting a further risk. If you are a regular user of gases at particular points, as in a laboratory, it is advisable to keep the gas cylinders in a safe compound outside and pipe in the gases through permanent piping. Good ventilation is also necessary.

Cylinders should be protected from damage by chaining them on to suitable trolleys. If you need the cylinders on an upper floor, check that they are carried safely either by lift or by two men. Cases have been known of cylinders being dragged – and banged – upstairs by one man. This is dangerous.

7

Is fire detection apparatus necessary?

If there is a fire, the sooner you know, the better. Install suitable fire detection apparatus but seek advice as to the type suited to your conditions. Your nose is also a useful auxiliary detector – never ignore a smell of burning.

A fire alarm which is linked to the fire station is likely to bring the fire brigade more quickly than a telephone call – people sometimes delay telephoning, because they underrate the danger, panic or misunderstand instructions.

In one department store, the telephone operator misheard the panicky tone of the manager who had detected a fire. She thought he said something else when he actually said: 'There is a fire!'. This led to several minutes' delay in calling the fire brigade – and a bigger fire.

When fires grow to disastrous levels, the cause is invariably either that they were not discovered in time or that they could not be successfully fought with the means available – personnel and equipment. The object is to detect the fire within a few minutes of its breaking out. There are various types of detection apparatus: some are designed to operate at predetermined temperatures, others respond to a rapid rise in temperature, others react to smoke. Before installing any apparatus, you should seek advice on the best type for your purposes.

The fire alarm itself should have a distinctive sound and should not, for instance, be a particular number of rings on the 'stop work' bell. It should be audible throughout the building. However inconvenient it is to stop work and vacate the premises when the bell sounds, you should always heed it. A problem can arise with oversensitive bells which produce a lot of false alarms. If you have such a one, get it rectified immediately.

At a university there was an oversensitive fire alarm bell. The academics and others became annoyed at the too frequent interruption of their work, so the practice grew up of ignoring it. Some did obey its call only to be laughed at by students and staff grinning from upper windows. Yet, if a fire *does* in fact occur in that building no one may be sure if it is real and this may lead to fatal results.

Have a plan of action for reacting to any fire which is detected and check the fire alarm every week: you may need it in a hurry, one day.

What about fire fighting?

The sooner a fire is tackled, the better. On site, fire extinguishing equipment may put out a small fire, if properly used, but is more likely to 'hold the fort' until the fire brigade arrives. People should not expose themselves to danger in fighting a fire and employees should be trained in the use of the equipment.

The kind of apparatus you need (e.g. fire hoses or fire extinguishers) requires some expert advice, for example, from the fire brigade. Install the right kind and number in suitable places where they are always readily accessible. They will need to be inspected regularly and refilled as necessary. In a kitchen, where materials are liable to burn, a fire blanket is useful.

Training

The need to receive training and 'hands-on' experience with fire fighting apparatus of any kind is real. This has to be arranged by you. The fire brigade may be willing to offer instruction if sufficient numbers of people are interested. If you share a building with others, they, too, should share in this. The worst time to learn how to operate apparatus is after a fire has broken out. Fires should be tackled immediately, not when you have had time to put on your glasses and pore over the small print on the label on a fire extinguisher – which are not all the same, incidentally.

A memorable demonstration took place on a supervisors' course on general management which included fire fighting. Unfortunately, owing to a prior engagement, the fire brigade member who usually came to give this demonstration could not do so, with the consequence that the lecturer decided to do it himself. After all, he had seen the fireman do it on previous courses . . . He started confidently, but the fire extinguisher nozzle took the initiative, gyrated above his head, discharging the energy stored up in the appliance. He struggled in vain to take control and only succeeded when the appliance had expended its contents. The trainees found this a refreshing change from the rest of the course and no doubt, whatever else they have forgotten, the memory of this remains with them.

7

Fire spread

Once it has started, a fire can rip through the premises in no time if you give it the right opportunity. Layout can be used to limit fire spread in various ways such as:

- isolate processes where highly flammable substances are used;
- use barriers (e.g. fire-resisting walls);
- avoid congestion of materials;
- keep doors closed at flammable-material cupboards;
- keep the premises and plant clean, clear deposits in dust extractors, remove grease from kitchen ventilators and cooker hoods.

If you have some heavy machinery, locate it on the ground floor if possible. If there is a fire which damages the structure sufficiently, heavy equipment is liable to crash through the ceiling.

Fire escape

Everyone in the building – customers and other visitors as well as employees – should be able to escape in case of fire, quickly and easily. Unless your firm is extremely small you will need a fire certificate from the local fire authority, so apply for one. This will be issued, certifying your escapes, once you have met their requirements.

All escape routes should be kept unobstructed. This seems obvious but may be overlooked.

One small Midlands company had just received a consignment of drums of flammable material but could not find sufficient space to store it. Then the manager had a brain wave and remembered that there was one quiet, unused space . . . the external fire escape. This is where the Factory Inspectors found the drums.

The fire exit doors should be clearly marked and kept closed. They should never be propped open – no, not even by a fire extinguisher! Even if yours is a very small firm you may need a copy of your part of a fire certificate if you are one of a number of occupants of a sizeable building. Check this with the owner who should hold the certificate for the building.

Fire drills are highly desirable though rarely popular – until you have a fire. Make sure everyone, including the newest recruit, knows how to get out in case of fire. Remember that there will be smoke and perhaps nasty fumes in a real fire. Consider also the safety of customers, contractors and other visitors to your premises. Once people are out of the building they should gather at a muster point for checking, so as to ensure that no one is left in the building.

Is security relevant?

Taking precautions against fire may – but usually need not – lead to security problems.

In a 13-storey building in the centre of a major city, the occupiers locked the ground floor fire exit because they feared that vandals might enter and create some havoc. The answer was to provide a door which could be readily opened from inside but not from outside.

Vehicles and other plant unavoidably left accessible should be immobilised, dangerous materials should be locked up and such other steps taken as are necessary to ensure that trespassers – and other visitors – cannot do damage to the plant or to themselves.

Checklist

- Know what the sources of ignition are
- Realise that almost anything will burn
- Control flammable substances
- Ensure care in the storage and use of gas cylinders
- Use fire detection equipment
- Have a plan of action in case of fire
- Call the fire brigade promptly
- Train employees in fighting fire
- Do not expose anyone to danger
- Ensure that your layout limits the spread of fire
- Provide and maintain adequate fire escape routes
- Arrange regular fire drills
- Have a head check at a muster point
- Secure premises and plant against vandals

8 Dangerous materials

What is a dangerous substance? □ Modes of attack □ Inhalation □ Permits to work □ Swallowing □ Skin contact □ Labelling □ Other modes of attack □ Precautions □ Flammables □ Sources of information

'The world alters as we walk in it' said J. Robert Oppenheim. This statement captures quite well the present time which has been described as 'an age of acceleration'. This reflects the many changes which are constantly taking place at an ever faster rate that man has difficulty in adjusting to them. The same applies to materials used in industry and business generally. New substances are constantly being synthesised, new uses are being found for old ones, new methods and plant are being developed, and new information about materials old and new is emerging.

That familiarity breeds contempt is a hackneyed statement but it well describes the approach of so many people to modern chemicals and other materials which have dangerous properties. Now that the garden shed houses so many 'nasties' everyone at home or at work is liable to become familiar with using, or seeing others use, pesticides and other dangerous materials.

What is a dangerous substance?

It might be said that no substance is safe in all its forms. Even water – for it can scald and engulf people who fall into it. But a special meaning has to be ascribed to it when dealing with practical hazards and risks at work. The term 'dangerous substance' has acquired a special meaning because modern legislation has developed greatly in this subject. All hazardous substances have to be controlled and there are important regulations on the matter (see p.110). There is a detailed definition of a dangerous substance in the COSHH regulations and if in doubt the best action to take is to make proper enquiries. Dangerous substances are defined to include:

●   substances listed as very toxic, toxic, harmful, corrosive or irritant;

- substances which have an official (HSE) maximum exposure limit;
- micro-organisms which pose a health hazard;
- substantial quantities of dust of any kind;
- other substances which create comparable hazards.

In more homely terms, a dangerous substance is one which has the potential for harming people's health. This it may do immediately as when someone is overcome by a gas like carbon monoxide (as emitted by car exhausts), or it may create deferred or chronic effects (for instance, lead may be built up in the body until a point is reached where lead poisoning manifests itself).

Modes of attack

It is useful in practice to know by what means a substance harms the body. At the risk of oversimplification, there are three main modes:

- inhalation
- swallowing
- skin contact

Inhalation

A wide range of dusts, fumes, gases and vapours are given off in various industrial activities. If inhaled, they may lead to lung diseases and other unwelcome effects such as eye damage, throat problems and wheezing. 'Dust' means substances in particulate form over a range of sizes down to the invisible ones which can be very harmful. Dust is produced in many industrial processes and in work such as rubbing down a lead-painted surface preparatory to repainting. This is liable to release harmful lead dust which may be breathed by the person doing it. Some materials are so dangerous that stringent regulations govern their use and disposal. Asbestos and lead are examples.

Asbestos

There are different kinds of asbestos including crocidolite which is called blue asbestos. In practice, care must be taken with all kinds of asbestos dust. If you encounter asbestos in your business you will need to seek specialised advice. Asbestos presents a serious breathing risk and this points to the type of precautions needed to prevent the dust entering the breathing air (e.g. containment and exhaust appliances). You also have to take great care in the disposing of asbestos. Merely using mechanical extraction appliances may create a neighbourhood risk by polluting the local atmosphere, so you must prevent the uncontrolled escape of asbestos. Special apparatus is required, bearing in mind that tiny, even invisible particles are dangerous.

Workers in garages

Work in vehicle-repair garages presents a number of asbestos hazards and those who work in them may be exposed to a slow development of one of the asbestos-related diseases, unless proper precautions are taken. Workers are exposed to asbestos dust especially when:

- cleaning brake assemblies
- cleaning clutch housings
- grinding brake linings
- drilling brake linings
- sweeping floors

8

   Garage workers should never blow dust out of brake drums or clutch housings with an air line, however tempting it may be to do so. Properly designed drum-cleaning equipment which prevents dust from escaping is available and should be used. Alternatively, drums should be cleaned with clean wet rags and the rags should be disposed of whilst still wet into a plastic waste bag. Never let them dry out where they can pollute the air with asbestos dust. Protective clothing should be provided for employees but they should not take it home. It is your responsibility to have it cleaned.

Cleaning floors

The item 'cleaning floors' may cause some surprise but, whenever there is a dangerous dust about, the sweeping of floors will stir it up into the breathing atmosphere of the workplace. Sweeping brushes should not be used, but either a special kind ('type H') of vacuum cleaner which does not return harmful particles to the air should be employed or, as an alternative, the deposits should be thoroughly wetted prior to scraping them up while still wet. *Ensure that asbestos waste is disposed of safely.*

Asbestos stripping

If you undertake asbestos-stripping work, you have to comply with extremely strict conditions of work and need a licence to start. This is obtainable from the HSE if they are satisfied about the standard of precautions which you intend to take. If you intend to start any business involving the use of or exposure to asbestos, it is imperative to seek authoritative advice beforehand. If you undertake demolition work, for instance, be on guard for encountering asbestos in your work (it was used extensively in old buildings for insulation purposes). It may also be present in all kinds of older equipment because it was abundantly used in the days before the hazard was fully recognised.

An unexpected encounter with blue asbestos took place when a firm was asked to renovate an Armstrong Siddeley car built in the 1930s. The vehicle body panels, floor and bulkheads had been lined with blue asbestos. A specialist asbestos removal contractor was – rightly – called in to do the work.

Owners of pre-war, veteran and vintage cars are warned!

Lead

Another widely used material which is met in various forms is lead. Like asbestos, it is subject to strict regulations. The main risk is inhalation but it may also be swallowed (e.g. if someone eats a sandwich without washing the hands first). This is because lead dust can lodge on the skin and under the fingernails. Lead is a cumulative poison and like all insidious diseases can too easily be ignored. It is up to you to ensure that safe practices are followed.

Lead is used in a multitude of work activities such as:

● high temperature work (over 500°C), as in shipbreaking;
● use of lead compounds producing dust, as in battery manufacture;
● abrasion of lead, giving off lead dust, as in firing small firearms in indoor ranges;

- spraying lead paint, as when painting bridges;
- working inside tanks which have contained leaded petrol, as in oil terminals;
- lead emission when testing petrol engines, as in garages.

Trichloroethylene

This is a widely used solvent and has a sweetish odour not unlike that of chloroform. Under certain conditions, it can produce phosgene – the 'war gas'. This is why no one should smoke near it, although it is generally regarded as non-flammable. To make matters slightly more complex, it has been found to be ignitable under some conditions, although they are rather special. In industry, it is employed in the degreasing of metal, wool and leather, and in quick-drying printing work. It is an ingredient of paints, waterproof cements and compounds, and is also found in insecticides.

A director of a newly-established company was working on his own when he went into a standard degreasing tank with the express intention of checking the bottom of the tank. There were only a few gallons of trichloroethylene there, but they were sufficient to cause him to be overcome. He collapsed and died before help arrived.

8

This illustrates the danger of entering a tank even when only a very small amount of solvent is present. Even if there is only sludge and the tank appears to be empty, the feet stir this up and release gas. Other solvents present similar hazards.

Permits to work

Where work has to be done inside any tank, pit, pipe or similar confined space where there is a risk of being overcome by fumes, gases or vapours, a 'permit-to-work' system may have to be used. This is a written system of authorisation signed by a responsible member of management allowing someone to enter the confined space under specified conditions.

The first step is to remove sources of the dangerous material (e.g. the liquid and sludge), then care has to be taken to prevent their ingress, and the space has to be properly ventilated. After satisfying himself or herself by testing that the space is safe to enter without breathing apparatus, the authorised person may issue the written permit to a particular member of staff, specifying the time limit to be spent inside the tank. If breathing apparatus has to be worn, the permit will say so and this must be of approved type. Where practicable, the person entering the tank must also wear a belt with attached rope, the end of which is held by a person outside capable of pulling the worker out in case of need. All the necessary equipment must be provided and this also includes suitable reviving apparatus which must be kept in good condition.

A tank had contained a substance which had been cleared out by feeding a solvent to it and draining it off several times. A check suggested that the original substance had been fully removed. As an extra precaution, the manhole cover was then left off for some hours for any fumes to dissipate. Then a workman leant into the tank probably to recover a tool he had dropped into it. He was overcome by fumes and never regained consciousness. A proper 'permit-to-work' system would have saved his life.

Fairly obviously, all the persons involved must be trained in the work they have to do and a sufficient number of people must be practised in the use of the apparatus, including that used for resuscitation.

Printed forms are used for permits, not scraps of paper as newcomers sometimes think. If you propose to do work involving entry into confined spaces you will need to seek advice first. Where an outside contractor is involved, precautions must be fully observed and their employees prevented from entering a confined space unless a permit has been issued.

In one case an outside contracting firm was doing work inside tanks for one of the big oil companies. This company had very strict rules with a 'permit-to-work' system and required the contractors to observe them in detail. Noticing that one of the contractor's men was about to enter a tank with his breathing apparatus slung over his shoulder instead of being worn, the oil company representative stopped the man and caused him to be disciplined severely for this breach of safety rules.

Swallowing

The mode of transferring lead dust from hand to mouth has already been described and, similarly, other poisons may be conveyed to the mouth. The precautions are, firstly, to minimise the risk of contact with the poison concerned but always accept that there is liable to be some on the hands. Care is needed and this requires careful washing. For this purpose, you have to provide good washing facilities, including warm water, soap and nail brushes. The workers must be required to use them before eating food or going home. This means that you have to provide a messroom of some kind for them to eat away from the workplace. Discipline is necessary to ensure that the precautions are followed.

One bad habit which can have tragic consequences is to put dangerous liquid substances into milk or squash bottles, or jam jars. Liquids should be kept in proper containers and always labelled with their contents. Manufacturers supply their products duly labelled also with the dangers and necessary precautions listed, but in the workshop it is all too easy to pour surplus material into any container which readily comes to hand. This is even sometimes done as a practical joke.

The workshop of a small factory was littered with mostly-empty lemonade bottles. But there were a few partly full and this served as an inspiration for a practical joker among the men. He added some trichloroethylene to one of these and waited for a workmate to come along to slake his thirst. This happened and the unfortunate man was taken to hospital and detained for a week. This illustrated not only the danger of unlabelled bottles, but also the responsibility management has to prevent horseplay. It was also an indictment of the standard of 'housekeeping' there.

8

Skin contact

Individuals vary in their susceptibility to skin complaints when in contact with chemicals and other materials. Of the many substances which attack the skin, only a few may be singled out, such as: mineral oils, soluble cutting oils, paraffin, white spirit, solvents generally and certain kinds of wood dust as well as the host of chemicals. Ordinary substances like flour can also cause skin problems which are generally classed as occupational dermatitis.

Labelling

Modern regulations have highlighted the need for careful and full labelling of dangerous substances. They require that certain terms are used more precisely for such purposes. Thus the words 'hazard' and 'risk' have been defined. The 'hazard' presented by a substance is its potential to cause harm (e.g. it may make you cough, may damage your liver or, somewhat dismissively, wipe you off the face of the earth). Clearly there are grades of hazard. On the other hand 'risk' means, in relation to a substance, the likelihood that it will harm you in the actual circumstances in which you use it. This will depend on:

- the hazard presented by the substance;
- how it is used;
- how it is controlled;
- who is exposed, to how much, for how long;
- what they are doing.

Drums and other containers of dangerous substances, under specific legislation, have to carry labels with hazard warning symbols and any of what are curiously called 'guidance phrases'. These are:

- R-phrases such as 'toxic by inhalation' and 'irritating to the eyes'
- S-phrases such as 'keep away from heat' and 'avoid contact with the skin'

The R-phrases thus refer to the nastier properties of the substance whilst the S-phrases give advice as to precautions to be taken.

All firms use dangerous substances, if only for cleaning purposes, so attention is drawn to the labels which are placed on them. If you produce dangerous substances, you will need to seek advice about the details of the regulations relating to the labelling of your products before despatch. Train your staff also to read labels and endeavour to ensure that labels are not obliterated as the contents of tins and other containers dribble over the side. Sometimes leaflets are provided by manufacturers or suppliers to give information and advice. Keep these for reference and refer to them.

Other modes of attack

The precise mechanism by which some substances attack the human being is not fully understood in some cases, but this is a matter for medical research. For our purpose, it is sufficient to know something about the adverse effects they produce and to bear in mind that precautions of certain types are necessary. Whether the mechanism is known or not, there is a miscellaneous and important group of diseases which can be suffered in:

- work with ionising radiations;
- work involving ultraviolet radiation;
- work involving infra-red radiation;
- work with sheep, cattle and poultry;
- work with the soil;
- work involving contact with rats' urine.

Precautions

Much has already been indicated about the necessary precautions which have to be geared to the nature of the particular danger. A list of common precautions may be useful at this stage, although not all will be pertinent to every substance. There is one overriding precaution, however. Always use the safest material that you can. Working with unnecessarily dangerous substances may sometimes seem good business because they may be cheaper, but the precautions need to be costed, too. Irrespective of money, the safest substances should be used: no one should be exposed unnecessarily to danger.

Listed precautions

- keep the minimum quantities on site
- keep the minimum quantities in the workplace itself
- store the remainder safely
- learn about the dangers – 'know your enemy'
- provide proper plant (e.g. suitable vacuum cleaners)
- provide suitable ventilation (e.g. mechanical extraction)
- maintain all plant and equipment
- incorporate safety into the methods of work
- use a 'permit-to-work' system
- train your employees in safe working
- monitor your employees' work for safety
- use disciplinary measures to enforce safety
- plan the layout to minimise dangers
- enclose dangerous substances as much as possible
- dispose of waste properly
- avoid discharging harmful substances into the atmosphere

- provide washing facilities of the requisite standard
- provide a place for eating food away from the workplace
- prohibit smoking where there is dangerous material
- provide protective clothing
- arrange for the storage and cleaning of protective clothing
- provide breathing apparatus or other suitable protection
- provide personal protection (e.g. safety helmets)
- provide barrier creams against skin problems
- observe the manufacturer's recommendations
- provide advice on dangerous materials which you supply to others

This list is not exhaustive and you will need to select those items which apply to your work. It will be a relief to know that you are unlikely to have to comply with them all, perhaps, in one small firm.

Flammables

There are many substances which are dangerous because they are flammable and/or explosive. The dust of many everyday substances can form explosive dust clouds. Examples are:

- wood
- cork
- grain
- sugar
- certain metals (e.g magnesium)
- some plastics

Explosions of dust clouds have produced some of the worst industrial accidents but lesser problems are known.
    Flammable gases, fumes and vapours include those given off by such materials as:

- LP gas
- benzene
- acetone
- carbon monoxide
- ether
- methane
- petroleum spirit ('petrol')

Petroleum spirit is dangerous both as a liquid and a vapour, and may harm the skin. Neither it nor substances like paraffin should ever be used to brighten fires because the liquid may then be splashed on to clothing which ignites, or the container may become involved in the fire and burst, and the fire may get out of control.

A self-employed car sprayer was clearing out a railway arch prior to leasing it for his vehicle-repair business. So he borrowed a 182-litre (40-gallon) drum to burn waste from the neighbouring premises. This contained some smouldering material to get a fire going. He walked over to the drum with a 23-litre (5-gallon) can of petroleum thinners – in which he had punctured some holes ready for a nice fire – and started to brighten the fire with the thinners. But Nemesis overtook him: he got his good fire but also an explosion in which he suffered 60 per cent burns.

Spontaneous combustion of rags soaked in some flammable materials can take place without warning if contaminated with certain flammable solvents. Flammable materials of many sorts have contributed to the known accidents.

8

An industrial painter was painting the inside of a pipe about 1.37 m (4 ft 6 in) in diameter, which was situated on a hillside with a slope of 1 in 4. An LP gas-powered lamp, used for lighting the work, was accidentally knocked over, rolled along and set fire to a paint tray which contained some bitumen paint. This was flammable with a flash point of about 32°C. The painter tried to escape past the flames but his paint-soaked overalls were ignited. Under the contract the painter's employer should have provided low voltage flameproof lighting. This would have prevented ignition.

Substances which are both dangerous to health and flammable include some of those already named such as carbon monoxide which can form an explosive mixture with air. Solvents generally attack the skin of susceptible people. In short, flammable materials are dangerous and all too often they also pose a danger to health.

Sources of information

One point which must emerge very clearly from consideration of dangerous materials is that you will be asking where you can obtain the necessary information. Sources of information include:

- labels and leaflets supplied with the products
- the manufacturers and suppliers directly
- the HSE directly
- the local environmental health department
- HSE publications
- trade associations
- trade publications
- specialist consultants

It is also hoped that this book will provide some of the answers and not merely the questions.

EMAS

Medical advice may be needed and the Employment Medical Advisory Service (EMAS) has been established to offer specialised advice and information of a medical nature. They are linked with the HSE and may be contacted directly or through the HSE.

9 Are your products safe?

Faults in domestic equipment □ Underlying principles □ Articles for use at work □ Substances for use at work □ Waste □ Erection and installation of plant

There has been a double revolution in this subject and things will never be the same again. Until the 1974 Act, manufacturers had minimal duties under work safety legislation, but that Act triggered the first revolution. The second one is the consumer revolution sparked off by consumer protection legislation. The latter is strictly outside the scope of this book but some reference is made to it here because it is linked with the safety at work legislation. From the point of view of a manufacturer and others now lumbered with responsibilities, the two areas of legislation overlap and to some extent have to be considered together. From the civil liability point of view you should note any changes which are introduced by the EC in coming years as they may directly affect your business.

Faults in domestic equipment

The public is reminded of the *consumer* aspect of safety law when it learns that a car manufacturer is recalling cars of a certain model for modifications (incidentally, many owners do not respond even though it will cost them nothing). Advertisements in newspapers are another way in which defects of domestic products are brought to public notice. They cover many items and are part of the consumer law, but have lessons for work safety. The following is a selection:

- faulty control device in electrical equipment which could lead to a lethal fire
- defective installation of certain central heating boilers
- defect in bottom bracket axle of bicycles
- risk of severe overheating in microwave ovens
- parts flying off a garden machine
- on/off switch of TV sets which can deteriorate rapidly and overheat so as to cause fire
- welding weakness in handlebar of tricycles

- freestanding cooker liable to topple over if door open and heavy load imposed on it

Similar examples under the criminal law are not easy to obtain for articles designed for use at work, partly because they are dealt with differently as when users are known and are contacted directly, or other trade contacts are used.

Before you as an employer feel reassured by this, it should be made clear that employers are still liable for the safety in the place of work however much at fault the manufacturer might be. As an employer you have duties to perform and if someone else is also at fault, this does not exempt you from your responsibilities. You both have to conform.

Underlying principles

Under the health and safety at work legislation, the objective is to ensure safety and health at the workplace. Under the consumer safety law, the aim is to protect consumers from adverse effects caused by products which they obtain.

Scope of the legislation

For safety at work, the duties are encapsulated in a section of the 1974 Act which is as laborious to read as it is important to understand. Some basic details need to be explained first.

Persons liable

To save constant repetition, the references are mainly to manufacturers but others have similar duties. These are designers, importers, suppliers and, with fewer duties, those who erect and install articles for use at work. The term 'suppliers' includes those who supply products by way of sale, lease, hire or hire-purchase (but not the finance companies dealing with hire-purchase), whether as a principal or an agent for another. If, for instance, your business is hiring out building plant, your job is not just to clean it up on return − however necessary that usually is − but to check it for safety too. When you hire it out again it should be in a safe condition.

Products

This is a convenient term which includes articles and substances for use at work. An 'article' in this sense means any plant such as machinery, equipment, appliance or components, designed for use at work even if it is used for other purposes too. There are no size limitations and an article might be a massive machine or a screwdriver for instance. In one recorded case, a number of imported mains tester screwdrivers were found to be faulty and potentially dangerous. An advertisement in the press sought to recall them all. In another case imported first-aid kits were found to be contaminated.

A 'substance for use at work' means any natural or artificial substance whether in solid or liquid form or in the form of gas or vapour, intended for use at work. As in the case of articles, substances do not need to be designed exclusively for use at work. It will be noted that the substances do not have to be dangerous ones as discussed in Chapter 8: *all substances are included.* The general intention of the legislation is that all products used for work are subject to the requirements being described here. The term 'at work' refers to work done in the course of employment by an employee and the time spent at work by a self-employed person. Domestic servants in private households are exempt from the 1974 Act.

It is convenient to consider articles and substances separately although the requirements are generally in parallel.

Articles for use at work

The duties of the manufacturer and others are:

- to ensure that articles are safe and without risk to health;
- to subject articles to testing and examination;
- to undertake any necessary research;
- to provide users with adequate information.

Ensuring safety

The standard is one of reasonable practicability, unless specific requirements are laid down (e.g. in legislation). This means that the risk has to be assessed (i.e. the chance of an accident occurring, its potential severity and so on) and set against the cost in terms of money and difficulties involved; then, a balance is struck. If you decide that a particular safeguard is not reasonably practicable, you must be able to justify your decision if challenged.

Noise is a matter which affects health and is to be considered in such assessments of machinery. Other items include controls, switches and a host of various matters in the design and assembly of plant.

A 40-feet-long earth scraper vehicle caused a fatal accident and much consternation in a motorway cutting when it charged driverless out of control. It had been restarted by its driver ready for refuelling from a visiting tanker. As the driver started it up, he was beckoned by the foreman so he switched off the engine to the tractor, leaving the one which drove the scraper running. On his return he found that the starter-motor would not operate – not an unusual occurrence. The driver tried what had become the drill for such a stubborn refusal to start: he agitated the gear-lever to and fro then, unsuccessful, he went to the tractor engine and started the motor by shorting the starter solenoid – also a normal practice in such circumstances. The scraper immediately lurched forward and ran driverless from bank to bank. In the emergency, another driver tried to climb into the cab but fell under one of the large front wheels and was killed instantly.

The official report after the investigation of the accident pointed out that there was a patent weakness in design in that such a large and sophisticated machine should depend for efficient operation on a flimsy and inadequate microswitch.

Testing and examination

This is necessary to ensure safety in use and much of it will take place at the production stage. Sometimes this work will already have been done elsewhere and the results will have been published. If you wish to rely on them, you need to satisfy yourself that they are appropriate and acceptable so as to relieve you of the need to repeat the testing and examination. Suppliers and importers may similarly rely on manufacturers' data and will need to justify this decision if challenged. Those who lack facilities may use outside laboratories and test centres for the purpose.

Research

Any necessary research has to be done by designers and

manufacturers with the objectives of (1) discovering any risks associated with the basic design and (2) eliminating or minimising hazards. Reliance may sometimes be placed on research carried out by others. Items like the following might emerge:

- safe working loads
- need for built-in safeguards
- adequacy of the electrical earthing
- methods of noise control
- safe operating speed
- specific precautions

Information

This plays a key role. The user – employer will need to have adequate information about hazards and precautions as he has to pass it on to the employees concerned. Each article will have its own list and no general guidance can be given. It is important that additional information is provided on request without delay. Sometimes information is best conveyed by an operating manual or even a leaflet. These should be written in clear language and cover the important items such as cleaning and maintenance as well as operating. Some food machinery, for instance, which has to be carefully cleaned for hygienic reasons needs both a suitable design and clear instructions as to how this should be done safely.

The purpose for which the article was designed should be made clear and instructions given regarding such matters as:

- how to operate, set, adjust and clean it
- emergency arrangements (e.g. rapid shut-down)
- regular maintenance
- periodic testing and replacement of components
- safe working practices
- use of protective clothing or equipment

Those who provide this information need to keep themselves up-to-date with the latest standards and to inform users as appropriate.

Transfer of responsibilities

Some obligations may, under strict conditions, be transferred. This applies, for instance, if a customer wants an article made to his specifications such as unfinished plant. But he must give a written undertaking to the other party that he will provide the necessary safeguards.

Substances for use at work

The duties under this heading are those of manufacturers, importers and suppliers. They are broadly similar to those already outlined for articles for use at work. One practical difference is that whereas with plant it is known what it is to be used for, generally this is not so for substances (e.g. a chemical substance can be used for any of a multitude of purposes).

Information about the substance's properties should be provided (e.g. toxicity, flammability, explosibility, reactions with other materials, etc.). Information should also be given about the precautions which should be taken (e.g. recommended handling procedures, how to deal with a spillage or fire, conditions of use to be avoided, etc.). The user should be supplied with any additional information as required.

Waste

It is not always realised that if you dispose of waste or waste products, or sell machinery second-hand you become a supplier subject to the same regulations. If re-use is not intended, the official advice is that this should be clearly stated in the contract of sale. If a substance is sold in a condition unfit for use this should similarly be documented.

Erection and installation of plant

Those who erect and install plant have to do so safely so that nothing in the way in which they do so creates a hazard. Examples of this point are few as the law has not been in operation very long, but the case illustrated below shows how careful tradesmen and others now have to be.

An electrician was convicted of manslaughter after a young father was killed by electric shock at his kitchen sink. The electrician had wrongly wired the electrical equipment for the central heating system. He had connected a live wire in the programmer to an earth lead in the junction box with the result that at certain times anything connected to metal pipework in the house was live.

This was a landmark case and the position now is that tradesmen and others need to beware. If anyone undertakes work for someone else and this results in someone's death, that person may be prosecuted for manslaughter.

9

10 Safe manual handling

Handling goods □ Causes of injury □ Accident prevention
□ Lifting techniques □ System of work □ Protective wear
□ Other factors □ Checklist

Handling goods

Goods – be they metal, glass, plastic, cloth, paper, foodstuffs or anything else are lifted and carried in every undertaking. They can be large or small, rigid or floppy, long or short; in other words, they come in infinite variety. Twenty-five per cent of all reportable accidents are caused by handling goods. Many are avoidable, yet each one is capable of inflicting lifelong injury. Painful backs, whether caused by accidents or not, lead to more days' absence from work than strikes.

The handling of goods includes lifting, lowering, carrying, pushing and pulling loads, and the latter includes all kinds of load – animate and inanimate. Handling patients in nursing homes, for instance, causes a large number of back injuries, many of which could be prevented by proper safety measures. There is evidence that many nurses leave for other work because of such injuries.

The factory legislation dealing with lifting and handling in general is hopelessly out of date and limited in concept. Several attempts have been made to update it and it will be replaced with legislation under the Health and Safety at Work Act. Current thinking is that emphasis is required to prevent, as far as possible, the handling of heavy loads without mechanical assistance. Where manual handling cannot be avoided, employers would have to take account of a number of factors. These include:

- the physical effort required
- the characteristics of the load
- the environment
- the nature of the task
- the workers' individual characteristics

Although these factors are in broad terms, their effect would be to require employers to:

- make a systematic assessment of manual handling tasks
- minimise their potential for injury
- provide mechanical handling equipment where possible
- provide necessary training
- provide information for employees
- provide supervision for them
- consult employees or their representatives about the measures taken

Causes of injury

There are many causes of accidents, such as lifting excessive weights or employing incorrect methods of lifting perhaps associated with underestimating the weight of the load. Even incentive methods of payment may play a part by urging employees to use unsafe techniques or to press on without waiting for help when needed.

The load itself may present inherent problems. For instance, 'live' loads can be difficult to handle as farmers and nurses will testify. Shock loads are to be avoided, such as the heavy sack suddenly thrust upon a man's shoulders. Containers with liquid sloshing about inside and long rolls of carpets present handling difficulties. Some objects are hard to grasp because of their shape, or an oily or sharp surface, or because necessary handles are lacking.

The back is the prime site of injury but all parts of the body may be affected, especially hands, arms, feet and legs. The immediate working environment may create problems (e.g. congested workplaces, stairs, ramps or roofs).

In a three-star hotel the young receptionist was carrying a tray of tea down a spiral stairway to the front office. She held the tray in one hand as it was light in weight but, missing her footing, she tumbled to the bottom of the stairs. Her injuries included multiple fractures and scalding. Yet the accident could have been avoided by a suitable handrail.

The total load moved in a day by an individual is important. Refuse collectors, for instance, may regularly have to lift and carry three tonnes weight in one day. Many workers do not have training in lifting techniques.

Joint lifting

When two or more persons are lifting jointly, they should act in unison, with the load equally shared between them and one of them should act as leader to coordinate their joint effort. All should use basic safe lifting techniques and, if possible, they should be of similar height and build.

Accident prevention

The first precaution is easily overlooked, yet it saves costs also – it is simply to do less manhandling. This may often be achieved by better layout and sequence of operations. The true cost of handling can be surprisingly high so it is worthwhile to check this point.

In one small works, liquid was drawn off a vessel near floor level into a bucket, then carried some 20 ft and lifted up to a bench where it was manipulated before being lifted again and carried to a machine some 10 ft away, then back to the bench, then to another machine about 12 ft away, then back to the bench before final operations making it ready for carrying to another area for packing. A lot of this manual handling could have been eliminated by better layout and all of it by well-designed but fairly simple mechanical aids. Costs would have been saved also.

10

Reducing the weight of loads

Often you can reduce the weight of an individual load carried by employees by changing the number of items put into a package. Customers who have to handle the packages (e.g. in retail shops) might welcome this too. Mechanical aids in great variety are available and should be used wherever appropriate.

Lifting techniques

Employees should be trained in at least basic requirements, especially:

- ensure that the route is clear beforehand;
- grasp the load firmly with palms, not fingertips;
- hold it close to the body;
- do not change grip;
- let the legs, not the back, take the strain;
- keep the spine straight;
- avoid jerking;
- never twist the body whilst picking up a load;
- lift in easy stages (e.g. floor to knee to start with);
- avoid overreaching.

System of work

The methods adopted for stacking, loading and unloading goods can create safety problems. Similarly the use of pallets – or the failure to use pallets – has been a factor in some accidents. The system of work is crucial.

Five workers in an engineering works were unloading sheets of steel plate from a jig standing on a table. Whilst two of them had gone to other work, unloading went on. Two of the remaining men unloaded the sheets by tilting them through the vertical, lowering them as far as possible, then allowing them to drop on the table. The charge hand on the other side did the same by himself, but the sheets 'took control', toppled on to him, causing fatal chest injuries.

The width of an object is important in determining the angle at which it can be grasped and, once above a critical width, the maximum acceptable load decreases rapidly. Sometimes the size of an item in relation to its weight prevents a proper grip. Is a handle needed? If so, is it in the correct position for handling? There is a risk of dropping a container especially a glass one if the surface is wet.

Protective wear

This is often essential and its nature depends on the type of objects to be handled. Safety boots with protective toe-caps are an obvious example. Everyone has ten toes waiting to be squashed if they are not protected properly . . . Hand protection, sometimes extending to the wrist or forearm, is necessary in handling goods with sharp edges. Gloves worn near moving machinery are generally dangerous as the machine may seize one quietly and drag the hapless wearer to his considerable detriment. If in doubt about the correct protective wear, seek advice.

Other factors

The immediate environment may be relevant to safe handling. For example, some men work inside industrial deep freezers where the low temperature may be allied to semi-darkness and perhaps worn flooring – a hazardous environment for handling goods. Do all you can to improve conditions.

The introduction of variability in the work has proved beneficial, i.e. the employee is given a change from lifting by being assigned a second job at intervals.

Training in correct methods is vital and there should be a periodic check at least to ensure that employees are following proper procedures. Older employees have less lifting power but this may be partly offset by increased skill. Young men often tend to lift excessive weights to demonstrate their strength. Above all, consider the introduction of mechanical aids – they exist in surprising variety.

Manhandling objects thus has a sinister side, inflicting cruelties on the vulnerable human frame, especially the back. The time will come when the use of people for much of this work will be regarded as obsolete and indefensible as machinery takes over. This will also further productivity generally.

Checklist

- Minimise the amount of manual lifting and handling
- Use mechanical aids
- Reduce the weight of individual loads
- Train employees in correct methods
- Provide suitable protective wear

11 Safe mechanical handling

What are the common hazards? □ Overhead travelling cranes □ Tower cranes □ Mobile cranes □ Derrick cranes □ Construction hoists □ Lifts □ Garage hoists □ Belt conveyors □ Slinging □ Checklist

Loads of all sizes, shapes, weights and types – including live loads like human beings and animals – have to be lifted, carried and lowered by machinery. There is an impressive array of machines for the many purposes and the scope for accidents is also on a generous scale.

Stories abound of cranes on North Sea oil platforms throwing themselves into the turbulent water with an expensive plop from time to time. On land, cranes and other lifting machines certainly do some remarkable things. Their favoured mishaps are overturning and dropping loads on whoever or whatever is beneath with a degree of irresponsible randomness.

It has been found that of the reported accidents few could be attributed to shortcomings in design and construction; the majority are, in fact, caused by human failures.

What are the common hazards?

Most mechanical lifting machines have certain errant forms of behaviour in common and these require broadly similar precautions. The risk of overloading has to be countered by a range of measures including the marking of the maximum or safe working load for the individual piece of equipment.

There are many relevant British Standards and other codes for the manufacture and safe use of lifting equipment. The HSE has published a specification for automatic safe-load indicators, primarily for cranes used in the construction industry. All such automatic indicators fitted to new cranes – whether new or existing models – must now comply with this specification or offer an equivalent standard of performance. All types of machines must be well designed and soundly constructed, of good material and be of adequate strength. Lifetime maintenance is essential. Periodic thorough examination by a competent person such as an insurance company's engineer/surveyor is required. Records have to be kept. Nevertheless, different types of machines have characteristics which call for special precautions. Only a few can be identified here.

Overhead travelling cranes

These versatile cranes have a wider variety of types of accident than any other as well as sharing the darker propensities of other machines. They can offer, for instance:

- electric shock;
- problems of access to the cab;
- limited visibility from the cab;
- possibility of knocking over nearby ladders and those who use them;
- mechanical hazards.

They probably have a greater risk of overloading in these days of heavier loads. For one thing, they are almost always installed in new buildings or in extensions. At the time of installation key decisions have to be made which may be regretted later. For example, the maximum load of the crane and the height of the crane's installation above the floor are matters which cannot easily be changed later as they are affected by the basic structure of the building. Older cranes had ladder access to the cab but today raked stairways are needed. The structural restrictions may make it impossible to install stairways.

A written procedure is needed for their operation and maintenance, and for work such as painting or cleaning which has to be done in close proximity to a crane. This requires a 'permit-to-work' system. The HSE is keen for such procedures to be attached to the firm's statutory policy statement.

Crane drivers should be carefully selected; a sense of responsibility, good hearing and eyesight are all needed. They should be trained and competent for the job and authorised by you or a responsible deputy to do it. You need to consider also having a second person available in case the regular driver is absent. A copy of the HSE's **Driver's Operating Card** which contains a checklist to be followed should be given to each driver.

All lifting operations need to be planned by someone who is experienced. It is necessary, for example:

- to ensure that the crane's height and capacity are adequate for the load;
- to ensure that suitable lifting tackle is available;
- to select the best route for the load, avoiding persons and obstructions;
- to give responsibility for controlling the lifting operation to one person;
- to check that either the driver has an uninterrupted view or provide a competent signaller to communicate with him.

Tower cranes

These monsters are common features of many a city's skyline. Particular problems arise when erecting and dismantling them. The important point is that this work must be done in accordance with the manufacturer's recommendations. Any suggested deviation must secure the manufacturer's approval first. It is also important that only proper manufacturer's parts are used.

If the manufacturer's handbook embodying the recommendations is a large volume it may be retained at the site office for reference. A short but accurate summary should then be provided for the use of those actually doing the work. Competent supervision at all stages is obviously needed. A sufficiently large clear area for stacking and handling the component parts will have to be provided.

11

A huge tower crane looming nearly 300 ft above a town centre street was lifting a six-ton jib from another crane which was being dismantled. But the lifting gear being used with it crumpled under the weight and slewed round out of control. One construction worker was injured while others leapt successfully out of the way. The falling jib just missed a crowded bus station.

Mobile cranes

The development of the modern massive mobile cranes has led to an increase in the number of accidents. Truck-mounted cranes have proved to be popular but their limitations have to be noted. The work they do is often carried out with outriggers and it is extremely important that these are extended to their correct position, which is sometimes marked on the plant. Some do not have a slewing range of 360 degrees and this needs to be taken into account when positioning the crane. Like other cranes, they need firm level ground for lifting operations. There should be an assessment of the conditions by management beforehand, and good training and supervision should be arranged.

A mobile crane was entering a customer's yard from the towpath of a canal up a slight incline. Whilst being manoeuvred, it started to roll backwards slowly until it rested against a barge which was consequently pushed away from its moorings. This allowed the crane to subside gently into the water. The driver had the presence of mind to abandon his charge on the first sign of trouble.

Derrick cranes

Fewer are employed these days but they are quite useful in handling comparatively heavy loads over a good operating radius. The ones still in use are generally old and lack modern protective devices, making the training of the drivers even more important. By now, all should have been checked for cast iron components which should have been replaced by parts as advised by crane specialists.

Construction hoists

The use of a checklist is useful for maintenance purposes. Below is a suggested list which the HSE has drawn up for a maintenance procedure:

- Hoistway enclosure
- Landing gates
- Cage or platform gates
- Electrical and/or mechanical interlocks on gates
- Cage or platform
- Suspension devices for the cage or platform and counterweight (ropes, chains, racks and pinions)

- Mast (including ties and locking bolts)
- Travel limit switches
- Guides
- Guide shoes
- Safety gear
- Winches
- Sheaves
- Bearings
- Counterweight
- Electrical (cables, conduits, switches, etc.)
- Buffers

Barrow or platform hoistways on building sites must be properly enclosed on all sides: the alternative is unacceptable.

A council employee was visiting a site to deliver some building materials. He happened to walk into a partly-fenced platform hoist when the platform with its load of tiles fell and struck him. Though front gates were provided, the sides and rear of the hoistway were open.

Inclined hoists are increasingly used and they have an impressive repertoire of the undesirable things which can happen. The precautions are detailed and you should seek advice if you use them.

11

Lifts

Passenger and goods lifts inside buildings present problems for regular users and others, including members of the public who have access to them. There are some familiar and basic safeguards such as interlocking devices on gates to prevent people falling down the lift shaft or being trapped between moving and stationary parts. There are also some less obvious hazards.

Lift maintenance requires careful planning and procedures. This work involves bypassing the interlocks (e.g. to gain access to the lift pit or roof of the cage). It is essential to make quite certain that no one else can enter the lift as the gates may be open or can be opened even if the cage is not at the landing. A safe system of work is essential to keep people away and this should include substantial barriers and warning signs to supplement them.

The installation of a new lift was almost complete. The lift could be operated from the lift motor room in the basement, from the controls in the lift cage and by pressing the call buttons at any landing. The landing doors, although fitted, were not yet working automatically. A lift engineer who was thought to have been checking running clearances was killed as his head was trapped between the cage and the top of the basement landing. It is all too easy when concentrating on something to be off guard.

A matter of some concern today is the use of domestic-type homelifts in nursing homes and residential homes for the elderly. They need something more robust for this purpose and some lifts in such premises have failed, sometimes with fatal results. It must be mentioned also that too many of these establishments still rely on human power for lifting instead of using more mechanical aids.

Garage hoists

Car vehicle hoists, as used in motor vehicle repair garages for working underneath cars, have had their own record of accidents.

A car was standing on a centre post vehicle hoist in a garage when the joint managing director was working under the vehicle with a mechanic. Suddenly the hoist crashed to the ground and trapped the director fatally. Investigation by HSE showed that the cause was lack of maintenance in conjunction with the bad practice of leaving the hoist in an elevated position for 48 hours over the weekend.

Belt conveyors

Widely used in moving goods and materials, conveyors of various kinds need to be assessed for safety. Among the special features is the need to provide access (e.g. bridges) from one side to another when long conveyors are in use. Otherwise people will climb over them which is dangerous even if the conveyor is stopped. The intakes of belts and pulleys are as dangerous as those of any machine but accidents tend to happen particularly when someone tries to clear away some material which is causing a jam. Maintenance personnel may be at risk if called upon to deal with adjacent machinery; or conversely, if dealing with a problem at a conveyor, they may be caught on nearby machinery.

A labourer received fatal injuries when he was trapped between the belt and tail pulley of a troughed belt conveyor powered by a 20hp motor. The belt was moving at 106 m (350 ft) per minute. What happened was that the labourer had reached between the belt and pulley with a shovel to remove some material from the pulley when the shovel and, as a consequence, his arm became trapped. The tail-pulley area was guarded only by a distance fence gate which was held in the shut position by a hand-tight bolt. A permit-to-work system was in fact operated at the conveyor but generally used only for removing blockages. The company was prosecuted and fined.

Slinging

Accidents due to poor slinging practice are a matter of continuing concern. Lack of training and inadequate supervision is blamed. HSE has released a video to supplement (but not supplant) training courses for slingers. This may be hired or purchased from:

> CFL Vision,
> PO Box 35,
> WETHERBY,
> Yorkshire LS23 7EX
> Tel: 0937 541010

It advises carrying on an actual slinging and lifting sequence as follows:

1. Know or find out the weight of the load
2. Select the correct sling
3. Fit the sling correctly, paying particular attention to the load's centre of gravity and the hitch of the sling
4. Make a trial lift and during this and the actual lift keep people away from the area
5. Set the load down in a clear area using bearers to support the load
6. Release the sling carefully and beware of chain hooks snagging on the load

7. After the lift, clear up the site and return the slings to their storage area

Checklist

- All mechanical lifting is potentially hazardous
- There are some common errors (e.g. overloading)
- Maintenance needs special attention
- 'Permit-to-work' systems are needed for some work
- Follow manufacturer's instructions (e.g. with tower cranes)
- Remember that the public — including children — may be exposed to risk
- Construction hoists are often inadequately guarded

---

12 Machine safety

Dealing with dangerous machinery □ 'Permit-to-work' system
□ Machine hazards □ Abusing machines □ Precautions □
Supervising employees □ Checklist

Dealing with dangerous machinery

Machines can be nasty, often biting the hand which feeds them.
They can be treacherous but usually require man's cooperation in
order to do their mischief. These tendencies sometimes may be
thwarted by good design but it is up to you, the employer, to tame
the machine and control the employee.

Duties are placed upon designers, manufacturers, importers and
suppliers but they do not relieve you, the employer and user, from
complying with current safety standards. Even if a new machine
is sold in a safe condition but you propose an unusual or ingenious
use for it, special precautions may have to be devised.

Different types of machinery

Fixed, power-operated machines are the run-of-the-mill machines
and range from power presses to dough mixers, from bacon slicers
to fairground roundabouts, being almost infinite in their diversity.
You may have to make do with older, second-hand machines, some
of which are obsolete in type and safeguards. Whatever they are,
old or new, you have to ensure that they are safe.

Mobile lifting machines

Mobile lifting machines are mainly dealt with in Chapters 11 and
13 but conventional hazards still occur like, for instance, dangerous
toothed gearing which will require guarding on any machine. One
of the main problems is proper earthing.

Foot- and hand-operated machines

Foot- and hand-operated machines can also be dangerous – as the
office guillotine demonstrates. Hand- and treadle-operated presses

12

are sometimes provided for use by domestic outworkers employed by firms which supply the equipment and raw materials. If you employ outworkers, ensure the safety of everything before it is handed over to the outworker. They need to be trained in the safe use of any machinery which you provide.

Computer-controlled machines

Computer-controlled machines are used increasingly and if you have them, you need to obtain expert advice about safety.

'Permit-to-work' system

For access to some machines a 'permit-to-work' system will have to be used in the same way as for access to confined space (see Chapter 8).

It is important to realise when a 'permit-to-work' system is called for, because sometimes this is not obvious until you give your mind to the matter. The underlying principle is that someone is required to do some work in a place which can be dangerous unless certain precautions are taken. The system has to be formalised in a written permission by an authorised person and addressed to a particular individual. This authorises entry to the place in question which is rendered safe for the duration of the work. Particular care is needed in planning the means of ensuring such temporary safe conditions: although sometimes a 'permit-to-work' system is in operation, it may be faulty in some respect.

The lack of a satisfactory 'permit-to-work' procedure cost a machine fitter his life. He was crushed between the fixed and moving parts of a hydraulic hoist used for lifting skips of metal blanks. Work was being done on associated and integrated plant which was on an automatic cycle. The movement of this cycle was initiated when the fitter reached into the hoist enclosure and accidentally broke the infra-red beam. This caused the hoist to rise and he was trapped.

The official report pointed out that the plant had not been effectively isolated and a satisfactory 'permit-to-work' system had not been operated.

Machine hazards

That machinery can inflict serious injuries is well-known. In *Household Words* (1855) Dickens refers to a grouping of manufacturers as an 'association for the mangling of operatives'. Conditions are better today, but there is little room for complacency.

Machinery is non-discriminatory in its aggressive habits, and will attack anyone within reach: its operator, the maintenance personnel or anyone else. Fingers, hands and arms are preferred but other parts of the body are also drawn into its hurtful embrace. It amputates, cuts, fractures, crushes, lacerates and bruises whatever is allowed to come within its grasp. It has to be respected.

It is impossible to list all dangerous parts, but a useful guide is to consider the matter under the headings of:

- intakes between two moving parts;
- traps between a moving part and a fixed one;
- direct contact with a dangerous part;
- other hazards.

Intakes between moving parts

These are exemplified by V-belt drives commonly used with electric motors; rollers like those of dough moulders in bakeries and intakes between chains and sprockets on many machines.

Traps

There are many traps between fixed and moving parts:

- the tool and die of a power press;
- top die and mould of a rotating-table pie and tart machine;
- the shearing action between revolving worms and their casings (e.g. of meat mincing machines);
- the closing plate and form of some printing machines;
- knife and bed of guillotines;
- beaters and framework (e.g. in trough mixing machines used in food, chemical and other industries);
- the blades of a ventilating fan with the casing;
- projections on revolving drums;
- reciprocating parts, such as planers used in engineering, which cause a trap with a wall or fixture;
- lifts which create traps as they travel up and down the lift well.

12

Direct contact and other hazards

Some accidents happen from direct contact with an inherently dangerous part such as revolving shaft, drill spindle or lathe stock bar. These are particularly treacherous because they look innocent, yet can wind into clothing or hair with a vice-like grip and cause grave injury. Direct contact with sharp-edged tools such as circular saws in woodworking, with set screws on revolving shafts, or with heated parts of plastic and other machines causes injury. Something can even shoot out of a machine, as when a circular saw or vertical spindle moulder ejects its workpiece at a stunning velocity. Electrocution may result from contact with unearthed machinery. Machines have even been known to fall over and the modern cartridge tool has been shot in the wrong direction before today.

Examples show how simple actions can lead to serious consequences. Some of the most distressing injuries are the result of a person's hair being caught in moving machinery. There is a very wide range of machines – including office equipment – which have the habit of quietly seizing strands of hair and winding it up some way, before its rightful owner is aware of the fact and this may be too late.

One girl, who had very long hair, kept it well out of the way as a result of strict company policy – at least as far as the nip between the belt and pulley of her machine was concerned. But one day she leaned forward to speak to the girl at the next machine. Suddenly she was conscious of her hair being pulled and struggled to release it. Unusually, the hair was released by the machine but not before she suffered severe shock and the loss of some of her hair.

Both men and women may be required to wear caps for safety – and hygiene – reasons but a cap is no substitute for machine safety. If you have parts of machinery which are dangerous you must fit them with secure fencing even if you also provide caps for employees. Incidentally, if you do provide them, remember that their design should pay some respect to current fashion and the feeling of dignity which everyone likes to have.

Among a machine's other tricks are overspeeding and, on occasion, ejecting parts of itself as when bits of a disintegrating abrasive wheel hurl themselves across a workshop.

Abusing machines

There are various ways of abusing machinery unintentionally, such as using the wrong machinery for a particular job. Improvisation has a long record of causing accidents.

In one case, a drilling-machine operator who was about to be made redundant, whiled away his time by polishing his own bowie knife on a buffing machine at work. He lost his balance and fell on the knife point. He was neither trained nor authorised to use this machine. The result was fatal.

The wrong machine may be used because the right one is not available; or because an employee misunderstands instructions, or is simply exercising misguided ingenuity – usually in ignorance of the hazards. It is a form of abuse of machinery to use domestic types for industrial or commercial purposes. Food processors and washing machines are known to have been used in industry where the demands put upon them are much greater than in the home and dangers can arise as a result. Larger output is required, rougher treatment may be expected to be meted out to them, and they may well not be robust enough for the use to which they are put. Above all, the safeguards may not reach the necessary industrial standards, and their use could be abruptly terminated by an inspector with a 'prohibition notice' issued on the spot.

A machine may be used in the wrong way, for example by failing to clamp a workpiece, or by misusing the safeguards provided, or it may be overloaded or overspeeded. Interfering with safeguards is regrettably not uncommon and may have disastrous consequences.

12

A fisherman was unloading fish from the hold of a fishing vessel by shovelling them into an elevator. While doing this, his foot was trapped between a down-running paddle and a fixed part of the elevator structure so that he was drawn into the machine. A second person tried to save him by pulling the safety switch but it failed to operate as it had been electrically bypassed previously by somebody unknown.

Another malpractice is to use a machine in an unsafe condition. Even without deliberate interference, machines may be unsafe especially if they have not been properly maintained. Accidents may be caused, for instance, by faulty brakes or controls, loose parts, badly-maintained guards or interlocking devices, and rusted or worn parts.

A foreman was killed by the top rim of the casing of a hydro-extractor flying through the air when the corroded and overloaded basket ruptured during use. The machine had been bought second-hand some eight years before. The basket wall thickness should have been 8 mm but had corroded to a mere 2 mm. The employer did not know anything about routine inspections.

To undertake maintenance work or cleaning machinery without proper precautions is foolhardy. The lack of a proper safety procedure can lead to accidents especially if this is done under pressure with production held up. (See Chapter 17.)

Cleaning machinery

Cleaning machinery leads to various kinds of abuse and maltreatment. A fundamental danger is that a machine may be deliberately cleaned whilst it is in motion, or, equally dangerously, it may be cleaned when it is put into motion by accident. The first is tempting because many machines are much easier to clean whilst they run. For instance, holding emery paper against a running shaft or spindle may look and feel innocuous but it is in fact a very dangerous practice: the hand and arm can be dragged in with resulting atrocious injuries.

Cleaning inside machinery which involves someone entering it presents hazards to the cleaner. Accidents of this type have happened over the years and still occur.

A 17-year-old factory worker went into a trough mixing machine to clean it with the machine stationary. Another employee came along and, not knowing that there was someone inside the machine, switched it on in order to discharge some of the product. The youth was killed.

The official investigation revealed that the machine was only one month old and had been provided by the makers with the necessary interlocking system. The normal type of interlock for these machines ensures that they cannot be set in motion until the lid is securely closed and locked by a special device in the closed position. Also it ensures that the lid cannot be opened until the machine has come to rest. A 'permit-to-work' system may also be needed. In this case the interlocking device was found to be faulty. The employer was prosecuted and fined.

Precautions

Guarding

Guarding is a prime precaution. Wherever possible, it should be fixed, and always well designed, robust and not easily removed. 'The careless workman must be protected', says the law. Unless a dangerous part is truly equally safe by virtue of its position, it must be guarded so as to prevent access even of a slim fingertip into the danger area. In some cases (e.g. for woodworking machinery) statutory standards are set out in detail.

Beware of apparently clever ideas like two-handed controls for they are often too easily circumvented by jamming a button down. 'Start' buttons and pedal controls should be shrouded to prevent accidental operation. 'Stop' buttons should be red and stand out prominently. The design of interlocked guards should prevent their being scotched. Such guards must be in the 'safe' position before the machine can be operated and, conversely, they must be designed so that they cannot be opened until the machine has come to rest. Proper maintenance is obviously crucial. Interlocked guards are distinguished from automatic guards which open and close to a preset pattern and which also need regular and careful adjustment.

Sophisticated guarding of photoelectric type is acceptable in some cases but you will need specialist advice. Similarly, where programmable electronic systems are used, specialist safety advice is necessary.

12

Other key precautions

Apart from guarding there are other important precautions you need to take:

● ensure that machines are suitable for the work in hand;
● avoid the use of domestic machines such as food processors – heavy-duty industrial machines should be used;
● maintain all machinery properly;
● keep adequate records of what has been done;

- locate machines properly (e.g. a fly press near a doorway has been known to bruise unwary passers-by);
- install machinery so as to prevent movement and toppling over;
- ensure that all electrical machinery and equipment are properly earthed;
- ensure that only authorised personnel work at any machine – and with no children around (even on farms) when machinery is running!

Proper use is obviously essential but failures occur.

A Scottish crofter was killed after falling off the bucket of a digger-loader. He was using it as a platform while helping to erect an electric light pole on to the gable of a neighbour's farmstead. The machine should never have been used as a makeshift platform.

Supervising employees

Employees at any machine need to be trained and supervised and you should always know what is going on in your premises. Every operator should know how to stop a machine even before he or she starts work at it. Young persons are prohibited from working at certain machines, and in other cases they can only be employed if they are either fully trained or are under proper instruction.

Care has to be taken when blockages in machines are being cleared. All too often the machine gaily starts up, irrespective of where the person's hand is. The importance of safety during maintenance is underrated (see Chapter 17). Cleaning machinery offers scope for abuse as it is sometimes easier to clean it when in motion but this is illegal and highly dangerous. At industrial meat-mincing machines, for example, a short burst of power helps to eject the meat from the point of exit but this may be at the expense of the operator's hand.

Loose clothing, dangling chains, finger rings, long hair and even straggly beards have tangled themselves with machinery and the machine always wins in such encounters. The precautions are obvious.

Checklist

- Do not rely on others where safety is concerned
- Provide and maintain proper guarding
- Ensure every machine's suitability
- Maintain it properly – and safely
- Earth electrically-driven machinery
- Ensure that only authorised personnel use machines
- Use machinery properly
- Train and supervise operators
- Ensure that machine cleaning is done safely
- Avoid loose clothing and the like

12

13 Safe transport operations

Road-type accidents at work □ What are your responsibilities? □ Other hazards □ Layout and environment □ The design of vehicles □ Operation □ Specific types of vehicles □ Dangerous goods □ Checklist

Road-type accidents at work

Transport accidents happen on business premises as well as on public roads, all the year round and usually with dire results. Most work accidents occur when vehicles are reversing, being loaded, unloaded or during maintenance and repair. They collide, skid, overturn, burst into flame and run out of control. There is one vital difference between road and work accidents: a public authority provides, maintains and controls public roads but not private ones. You – or your landlord – do.

What are your responsibilities?

The use of your vehicles on public roads is outside the scope of this book. But what about your own premises? Many small firms have only a yard, or even a shared yard, for the reception and despatch of goods, and some have none. Some have complete road systems (e.g. caravan sites and leisure parks). Whatever the size and nature of your premises, you have some responsibilities for traffic safety there.

You need to consider matters like the design, maintenance, repair and use of all vehicles which you operate and the safety of pedestrian movement within areas under your control. The training and competence of your drivers are matters for you. There are a number of special regulations for certain dangerous loads which you carry and you need to identify those which apply to your work. These are beyond the scope of this book.

Other hazards

There is a risk of electrocution where vehicles with raised parts, such as tipper lorries or mobile cranes, come in contact with overhead electricity transmission lines. In vehicle maintenance, work hazards are found in garage repair shops (e.g. the risk of tyre bursts especially with wheels with locking rims).

In one small factory a visiting sales director had his legs broken when the factory mechanic was changing a tyre without taking proper precautions. The locking rim flew out and struck him violently as no protective cage was used.

A major accident producer is the lift truck, either used indoors or outdoors. Employees going about their ordinary work are often unaware of the possibility of sudden danger from a truck which creeps up on them. Although fork trucks are by no means silent in operation, they are commonly used in noisy environments. When they push their way through swing rubber doors in a factory, for instance, they appear to arrive out of nowhere; that's why workpeople need to be particularly wary in such places.

The routes and operational areas for trucks need to be planned with safety as well as production in mind. For example, diesel-engined trucks (and other plant) should not be employed in places where there is a flammable atmosphere as in paint manufacture or where solvents are used, without special precautions. They also emit toxic gases and there must always be adequate ventilation where they are used.

Hazards to be noted are: (1) direct ignition of the surrounding flammable atmosphere (e.g. from hot sparks from the exhaust); (2) the presence of flammable atmosphere in the air intake of the engine. This can have dangerous consequences which will surprise everyone who is unaware of the probable effects. The engine is liable to accelerate out of control causing overspeeding and possible flashback through the intake to ignite the surrounding flammable atmosphere. In extreme cases, the engine itself may be destroyed. Even turning off the fuel supply may not stop the engine as it may continue to run on the ingested vapour. There are precautions which may be taken but this is a matter on which you are advised to take expert advice.

Many, perhaps most, accidents are similar to transport accidents generally but one difference is that workpeople may not be thinking about traffic at all as they go about their ordinary business.

The yard foreman at a container handling and repair depot walked into the side of an articulated trailer and tractor unit which was executing a tight turn and was run over by its rear wheels. The explanation was that he was concentrating on some papers he had in his hands.

At the heart of transport accidents at work, according to official reports, lie organisational defects, unsafe vehicles, faulty systems of work, inadequate training of drivers and a degree of ignorance and indifference by those involved, including managers.

Layout and environment

Vehicles often have to operate in places where there are blind corners, excessive gradients, inadequate turning room and poor lighting. The presence of pedestrians adds to the problems. Sometimes they cannot be easily seen but this is no excuse for running them down. It is up to you to assess the problem and deal with it before any accident happens, bearing in mind that members of the public might stray into workplaces.

At a disused airfield there were some small factories. Vehicles visiting them used to turn round at a large roundabout there. Neglect had caused blackberry bushes to spread into the roadway for about 1.2 m (4 ft), which should have put drivers on their guard. The driver of an articulated vehicle on the roundabout failed to notice a tramp in the bushes and drove into him.

13

The layout of any yard, road or road system should be safe. Is the entrance shared by vehicles and people, including customers and other visitors? Can you not separate them? A one-way system, if feasible, has much to commend it. Can you control the movement of people better? Any traffic and warning signs used have to conform to the Signs Regulations. Many sad tales can be told of accidents at loading bays and areas. A simple step is to ban workpeople from the loading area unless they work there.

Reversing vehicles

Reversing vehicles contribute to deaths and injuries at work. There should be adequate turning room for vehicles or, if possible, you should ensure that the driver reverses only with an assistant to guide him. Check too on the visibility conditions when it is dark.

At one retail store, articulated vehicles had to back up to a loading dock across a public car park. In spite of a risk of pedestrians (including children) being in the way, the drivers often reversed without an assistant. If the management had checked, they would have noticed that the otherwise excellent overhead lighting was obscured by the high vehicle which had to back up blindly to the dock in the dark.

Construction sites

On construction sites, especially where there are several subcontractors at work, traffic movements need to be well organised. The entrance and exit points should be planned as well as the places for depositing loads. Noise on building sites is such that men working there may not hear traffic approaching.

Road maintenance

This has been described as one of the most difficult areas of transport safety because road works constitute a risk not only to the construction workers but to road users. A balance has to be struck between the safety needs of the two groups. Many serious accidents have occurred and it needs little imagination to envisage the result if a vehicle travelling at speed crashes into a road works site.

Two main principles have been and are still being considered. One is how best to keep non-works vehicles out of the site. The other is how best to prevent workers, materials and equipment from the site encroaching on to the carriageway being used by road traffic. Road signs relating to road works constitute one means of control but it is vital that the person in charge of the site knows exactly how to set them out. The standards are described in a Department of Transport document, *The Traffic Signs Manual*. All drivers will have seen some wrong and misplaced signs at times, but safety demands the proper use of the right signs at all times – and their prompt removal after the works have ceased.

Vehicles operating indoors

For vehicles which operate inside buildings, broadly similar principles apply as for outdoors. A basic safeguard is to paint white lines to indicate vehicle routes, and the storage of goods should never be allowed in the path allotted to transport. If there are dangerous materials about, care is needed to ensure that they do not adversely affect the use of works transport. For example, LP gas should not be stored where a vehicle could accidentally strike the storage tank or cylinders.

Charging batteries

Charging batteries for lift trucks should be done in designated areas as this releases hydrogen which is liable to produce an explosive mixture.

In one case a battery had been taken off charge and was being fitted in a vehicle by a mechanic. His spanner, used to tighten the connections, slipped out of his hand and sparked off the oxygen–hydrogen mixture from the battery. An explosion shattered the battery case, pieces cut the man's face and he was splashed with acid.

13

The design of vehicles

Check whether a particular vehicle is designed for the carriage of passengers and, if not, enforce a ban. Sometimes a safety feature is necessary such as the roll-over bar for a tractor. Many dumpers still have starter handles with their built-in danger of kick-back whilst being turned. Their replacement by electrical starters would save many injuries.

Never modify a vehicle without the manufacturer's approval. For instance, fork extensions should not be attached to fork-lift trucks without the manufacturer's agreement. Also some users have increased the counterweight with the intention of handling heavier loads without realising that this could lead to instability.

Good visibility for the driver is one of the most important needs as far as operational safety is concerned. The following factors, among others, should be considered:

- seating position of driver in relation to the layout of the vehicle and its superstructure or bodywork;
- devices to improve visibility such as Fresnel lenses and, for the rearward view, mirrors and radar or television units;
- wiping and washing facilities for windows and mirrors.

Poor standards of maintenance continue to be a significant factor in the cause of accidents. For instance, while construction vehicles used on the public highway are usually reasonably well-maintained, similar ones on sites tend to be less well-maintained. Obviously, routine maintenance is essential (e.g. checking the brakes frequently). Records should be kept of all work carried on under the heading of 'maintenance' and they should be legible and complete.

Operation

As road accident statistics show, careful driving is not second nature for the human race. As an employer you should select your drivers carefully ensuring that they are competent to operate the vehicle they have to drive. On construction sites, for example, no one under the age of 18 is allowed to operate any vehicle. No one should operate any vehicle without express authorisation. Special regulations apply to road tankers and to the carriage of dangerous loads on the roads. These need to be consulted if they apply to your business.

Specific types of vehicles

Lift trucks cause many accidents and about 45 per cent of them are officially classed as due to operator's error. This emphasises the need for careful selection, training and supervision of operators. Fork trucks show no mercy to operators who maltreat them or even fail to park them safely.

A battery-operated fork-lift truck was used in a factory to move parts on pallets from one machine to another. Whilst waiting for a pallet to be loaded, the operator left the machine unattended. A pallet nearby, standing on its end, fell over when it was accidentally knocked, striking the long control-handle of the truck. This galvanised the truck into action which struck the unsuspecting girl who was loading the pallet for the truck. The driver had failed to set the main switch off and there was no 'dead man's handle'.

Dumpers

As they chug round building sites, dumpers look easy to operate, especially the small ones, and are welcomed as useful things to have around. But any benign appearance is misleading as they will play high jinks, given half a chance. The dumper has a special ability for turning over and depositing its driver, itself and the load in an unceremonious manner wherever it chooses, whether reversing or not.

On one building site some bricklayers decided to take a dumper to save them time in their work. One of them, an untrained driver, loaded it with mortar and set off to the place where it was wanted. He travelled down a 1:8 gradient, apparently out of gear; the dumper gathered speed but the driver managed to steer it into a bank of earth. This threw him off and the dumper, true to its nature, decided to fall on top of him.

The danger has become such that a special handy card has been published by the HSE to give to dumper drivers. It emphasises safe operation and advises them

- to check the brakes before use;
- to turn the starting handle properly to avoid injury;
- to operate the machine carefully.

This is a reminder and not a substitute for adequate training and supervision. You also have to ensure that the particular type of dumper is suitable for the work in hand, is properly used and well maintained. Records of maintenance should be kept, as with other vehicles (see Chapter 19).

Freight containers

Regulations spell out fuller requirements than can be summarised here and should be consulted. Some of the basic ones are that they

13

must be of an approved type (and so marked), properly maintained and thoroughly examined periodically. Some of the essentials when they are used in harbour areas are:

- preplan the packing of goods in them to ensure compatibility of the contents with one another and to protect those who will have to unload them later;
- prevent overloading;
- check emptied ones before reuse to ensure that the previous load did no damage (e.g. by leaking corrosive substances which would affect the next load);
- take preventive action against the violent opening of doors once the doorlocks have been released. This can happen because of compression of the cargo or the use of air bags as dunnage between cargo and container walls. If pressurisation is suspected, the HSE recommends the placing of a lift truck against the doors to facilitate a more sedate opening.

Dangerous goods

The transport by road of dangerous substances in containers such as drums, bottles, carboys, cartons or skips as well as road tankers as such, is now subject to strict international-type regulations. They cover such matters as the design, construction and maintenance of the vehicles used; the provision by the consignor of information about the load; the carrying of that information by drivers; their adequate instruction, obligations on loading, unloading and stowage; the fitting of orange warning plates on vehicles; and supervision and safe parking of vehicles carrying larger quantities of dangerous substances or any amount of self-reacting substance.

There are details and strict rules for road tankers and tank containers used for the conveyance of dangerous substances by road.

Wherever dangerous substances are to be carried by road you are urged to check the legal requirements with your trade association or other source of expertise.

Checklist

- Treat all vehicles as dangerous machines
- Plan a safe layout for them on site

- Plan the movements of vehicles and pedestrians
- Maintain vehicles in a safe condition
- Do not modify the design of a vehicle without the manufacturer's agreement
- Check the safety of freight containers
- Select, train and supervise drivers and operators properly

14 Pressurised systems and other plant

Pressurised systems □ Electrical safety □ Visual display units (VDUs) □ Checklist

There are too many types of plant to be discussed in a small book and the items chosen here are, firstly, pressurised systems and, secondly, electrical installations. Both are widely used and are now subject to regulations made in 1989 – 90 which may not be familiar to those who operate small firms.

Pressurised systems

The regulations are designed to protect people at work from the risks posed by uncontrolled releases of stored energy from pressure systems. They replace previous patchy and outdated legislation, and introduce a logic into the subject by covering all and not just some plant in all places of work. Hitherto only a few types of pressurised plant were covered and only if they were in certain sectors of industry.

Types of plant

The range of plant covered is wide and has special relevance not only to the chemical industry but also to non-industrial premises. Familiar examples are steam boilers, compressed-air systems (including air receivers and associated pipework) and large refrigeration systems which are widely used in commerce and the retail trades. Small steam plant, for example, is found in many catering establishments and other types of pressurised plant is used for drink dispensing.

Application

The new regulations impose safety requirements with respect to design, construction, installation, repair, modification and use of pressure systems and transportable gas containers at work. The intention is that all parts of pressurised plant (including the interconnecting pipework and fittings, protective devices and control equipment) should be regarded as a single pressure system. This is necessary because safety is critically dependent upon the integrity of the whole system. 'The chain is as strong as its weakest link', it might be said.

Detailed requirements

The regulations, in accordance with modern practice, set out the broad objectives, leaving the details to be dealt with elsewhere. In practice, the details are spelt out in *Approved Codes of Practice* issued by the HSE together with *Guidance Notes* published to supplement them. If you have pressurised plant, and many small firms have, you will need to obtain the relevant Codes of Practice from HMSO. There are two: one for pressure systems as such, and one for transportable gas containers.

Written scheme

A characteristic of the new arrangements is that, if you have the plant in question, you will have to draw up a written scheme setting out the details of necessary examinations of plant and the intervals between them. The pressure systems code sets out in detail how you should go about deciding the scope of the scheme as it applies to you. For this, you will need the advice of a competent person and the code sets out acceptable criteria for persons certifying and drawing up such schemes.

Gas cylinders

One approved code deals with gas cylinders of which there are an estimated 30 million in this country. As the Chairman of the Health and Safety Commission has said, 'They are all miniature pressure vessels and some operate at very high pressure'.

The code sets out in detail how cylinders should be stored and handled to reduce risks. Also it includes the precautions necessary at filling plants to ensure that only cylinders fit for further service are refilled. See *Safe Pressure Systems* (IND(S)27(L)) obtainable free from HSE Public Enquiry Point at Sheffield, Bootle or London.

Electrical safety

After decades of working with old regulations, the legislation is now up-to-date with the coming into force of the long-awaited Electricity at Work Regulations of 1989. Electricity does not just mean a shower of sparks if it goes wrong, the HSE points out. Shock, burns, flame and explosion can result from taking unnecessary risks. Cable strikes can mean misery for thousands of people as workers digging on building sites hit underground electricity cables – often at personal risk.

The regulations apply to all employers, self-employed and employees, and extend protection to about 16 million more people than the old legislation. Work on such places as research establishments, schools, farms, and domestic premises are all now under this protective umbrella. Industrial establishments will of course be covered but to a higher standard than before. The regulations set out basic electrical safety principles as opposed to detailed requirements. Good practice must always be followed. One point which is greatly emphasised is to switch off first before working on electrical equipment. Two Approved Codes of Practice accompany the regulations and are obtainable from HMSO. Reference should also be made to current regulations of the Institution of Electrical Engineers.

Two points to emphasise for small firms are, firstly, only those who are electrically qualified should deal with electrical faults and installations. Secondly, electrical installations should be periodically checked for safety by qualified personnel. For electricians there are rules for protection especially where live working is unavoidable.

Visual display units (VDUs)

14

VDUs are widely and increasingly used in offices and elsewhere. There have been reports in the media of adverse health effects among operators. In particular, complaints have been made about eye troubles, headaches, skin rashes, aching arms and shoulders, and even harm to unborn children of pregnant operators.

VDUs do give off a package of radiations but in modern models in general they should present no hazard according to the latest expert opinions. The National Radiological Protection Board is reported as saying that most of the radiations are well below acceptable levels. It is important to maintain the equipment properly and remedy any flicker promptly. The Association of Optical Practitioners has said that VDUs do not cause damage to operators' eyes but the nature of the work makes them more aware of existing eye deficiency. Eyes deteriorate with age and VDU operators share this characteristic. There has been a report that gas-permeable contact lenses can be adversely affected by electro-magnetic radiation from computer terminals.

Skin rashes, it seems from official reports, are limited in number and affect those with sensitive skins only. Any aches in arms, wrists and shoulders are ascribed to the whole workplace set-up. The principle is that a workplace should always be designed to adjust to the worker but all too often – and not only with VDUs – it is the other way round. The operator may find the seat too low or not adjustable; the worktop may be the wrong height; the screen too near or too far; the screen characters too small or otherwise hard to see clearly. The focus of the eyes is fixed for too long periods unless steps are taken to prevent this (e.g. by placing pictures or plants in the room so that the eyes may focus on them for a change from time to time). Bad lighting such as excessive contrast, glare and reflections may be evident and temperature and humidity unsuitable. There may be noisy printers near to add to the stress.

All such matters require attention and the solutions are largely obvious. Where pregnant operators are worried about hazards, real or not, they should have the option of moving to other work on request. For all VDU operators, regular rest pauses are highly desirable and they should not be employed too long without a break or for too many hours in any day.

At the time of writing, an EC Directive has recently been adopted which will lead to statutory regulations in due course. It sets out requirements for such matters as

- display screens
- keyboards
- furniture
- lighting
- working environment
- rest breaks
- eye tests.

The last word has not been said about VDUs yet, and their design may change in future. This may affect health and safety, so it is important for you to keep up-to-date with matters if you employ anyone on VDUs.

Checklist

- All plant safety needs to be checked
- Identify your pressurised plant
- Obtain the relevant Codes of Practice
- Draw up a written scheme
- Ensure that it is observed
- Ensure electrical safety
- Keep conditions for VDU operators under review

14

15 Safety management

Safety as part of management □ Policy □ Accident prevention
□ Control of dangerous substances □ Policy statements □
Conclusion □ Checklist

Safety as part of management

The impact of safety legislation on small firms is a subject of
importance nationally as well as to the firms themselves. The
significance of health and safety at work from the viewpoint of any
undertaking, large or small, is that it is part of the function of
managing. Safety – which here, as elsewhere in this book, includes
health – is not an optional extra to be added when funds are ample
and time is available. It is required right now: it is an inherent strand
in the cloth of management.

When you plan and organise your business, draw up your budget,
recruit and train staff, give orders and monitor the work being done,
the safety implications are part of the decision-making process. If
you sell or hire out products, you similarly must consider safety
together with other relevant matters. It is compulsory to insure under
the employer's liability law once you employ anyone. This is done
through one of the insurance companies which undertake this
business. The penalties for failure are particularly severe. The
Certificate of Insurance should be displayed in your premises.

The HSE has publicly stated that it seeks to strike a balance
between overburdensome enforcement on the one hand and the
erosion of the law for financial reasons at the expense of employees'
health and safety on the other. Each employee of a small firm should
not be at greater personal risk than if employed by a large firm.
If you lose your hand in a machine, it is the same personal disaster
whether it happened in a small or a large concern.

You who are in charge generally control the environment in which
all your employees will work and obviously this must be acceptable.
You mastermind their conditions of work even though you may
consult your workforce, which can be helpful. But all this brings
responsibility. The responsibility of deciding not only the quality
of working life your workforce shall have, but also the impact your
business will have upon the local community (e.g. pollution).

15

Policy

You have a safety policy, however vague, simply by your intentions expressed in action − or inaction. Is your policy towards employees, customers and the public generally what it ought to be? Some specific decisions have to be made. For instance, do you intend to employ young persons? If so, are you prepared for the extra training these inexperienced youths must have? You may decide to employ persons over retirement age, part-timers, married women 'returners', non-smokers or some other particular group. You make decisions of many kinds but must heed the safety implications. (See p. 112 for statutory policy statements.)

Accident prevention

In planning your activities, consider what is meant by 'safety' in any particular context. There is misunderstanding, for instance, about the difference between accident prevention and safety. Accident prevention means what it says. Safety is a wider term and embraces accident prevention and damage limitation, that is dealing with the consequences of accidents if they do occur. A guard for a machine is an accident-prevention measure but first aid is a damage-limitation one. The exclusion of sources of ignition from the workplace is an example of accident prevention but fire extinguishers are classed under the heading of damage limitation.

The basic safety rule is that you need both to prevent accidents as far as possible and to deal with the consequences if an accident does happen. This may seem obvious but it is often overlooked.

Control of dangerous substances

It is compulsory for employers and self-employed persons to comply with regulations in force since 1 January, 1990 which glory in the acronym COSHH. These are the Control of Substances Hazardous to Health regulations.

There is a wide range of substances available today which are capable of damaging health − and not by any means only in industry. Some are used, for instance, in the painting and decorating trade, in farms and educational establishments. No work which is liable to expose anyone to hazardous substances may lawfully be carried on unless an assessment has been made and necessary precautions have been taken. This involves:

- evaluating the risks;
- deciding what has to be done about them.

A sensible step-by-step approach is needed.

A dangerous substance

Under the COSHH regulations, this term has a special meaning. It includes those substances which are labelled as dangerous (i.e. very toxic, toxic, harmful, irritant or corrosive), agricultural pesticides and other chemicals used on farms, and a range of other substances for which occupational exposure limits have been set. Harmful micro-organisms, substantial quantities of dust and, indeed, any material, mixture or compound which can harm people's health are also included. Because other regulations govern them, asbestos, lead or ionising radiations are excluded.

The printing industry, for example, has quite a number and illustrates the kind of substances to consider: inks, varnishes, reducing solvents, blanket washes, ink strippers, adhesives, plate and photographic developers, activators, fixers, deletion fluids and cleaning solvents are all included.

Whatever the type of undertaking you have, you must make an assessment. This is done by a step-by-step approach:

- identify the hazardous substances (e.g. by labels or ask suppliers);
- consider how the substance is used;
- find out the means by which it can harm people (e.g. on skin contact);
- check storage and handling arrangements;
- consider what might happen in accident or emergency (e.g. spillage);
- compare your standards with those generally accepted (see below);
- decide what you have to do to control the hazards discovered;
- consider whether you can 'do it alone' or need expert help;
- make a written record of your assessment;
- review your assessment from time to time.

15

The problem of comparing your findings with what is generally accepted does not mean checking on what your competitors are doing. They could be quite wrong. The standard which is acceptable is that agreed to by the HSE and medical profession. There is an enormous amount of information on the matter and your trade association, chamber of commerce or professional institution should be able to advise you. The HSE is ready to give advice on request. Or you may decide to employ a consultant. In that case, make sure that the consultant is of high standing and enquire beforehand about the cost.

Having carried out the assessment, you have to ensure that the necessary steps are taken to control the hazards:

- control exposure to exclude or, if impossible, to minimise the risk;
- check that the means adopted are effective;
- ensure that they are properly maintained;
- arrange for monitoring of substances to maintain proper limits;
- keep records of monitoring;
- train and instruct employees about the risks and precautions.

Further details and advice are available from HSE and other bodies as already indicated. In addition, the HSE has published a series of leaflets and a booklet to help you. The main one is *COSHH Assessments. A Step-by-Step Guide to Assessment and the Skills Needed for It.*

Policy statements

The 1974 Act requires every firm where five or more persons are employed to draw up a written policy statement. The objects are:

- to set out your policy on health and safety;
- to state the organisation and arrangements for carrying it out.

Once more to help you, the HSE has published a useful document entitled *Our Health and Safety Policy Statement* which is obtainable from HMSO. By entering the details of your firm's organisation and arrangements in the spaces provided you can produce your policy statement without too much difficulty. It will make you review matters and as such is a useful exercise in itself. This statutory policy statement must be kept available for inspectors. A summary of the main subjects may be useful:

- a general statement of policy – signed by you;
- a list of responsibilities (e.g. of those named as responsible for some area of safety);
- accident arrangements (including details of first aid);
- general fire safety;
- address of HSE or other inspector and advisors (if any);
- special training arrangements;
- your house rules for contractors and other visitors;
- notes on hazards (of all kinds);
- housekeeping arrangements (including waste disposal);
- rules for electrical safety;
- dangerous plant and necessary precautions;
- dangerous substances and relevant precautions (not only those substances subject to COSHH regulations but also flammables etc.);
- other important hazards such as on-site transport vehicles.

Once completed it is necessary to keep it up-to-date. This will be needed if personnel named in the statement changes or new plant or materials are used, for instance. In any case a periodic review is required. If you prefer, you can use your own format and disregard the printed one, but most small businesses will find this document very helpful. The policy statement must be brought to the notice of all your employees as must any revision of it.

Conclusion

The underlying philosophy of the health and safety legislation today is that of self-regulation. As an employer you have to consider health and safety in your decision-making. This book aims to help you in this. But you will need to keep yourself informed and up-to-date. Things are constantly changing and, to give one example, robotics will be more common in small firms one day. Perhaps in yours.

15

You set standards and it is the discipline you enforce which is so important in ensuring safety. Your decisions directly affect the quality of working life as far as your employees are concerned. It is a responsibility placed on management and this book's aim is to guide you in this.

Checklist

- Remember that safety is an inherent part of management

- Distinguish between accident prevention and damage limitation
- Do your COSHH assessment
- Use a step-by-step approach for this
- Find out what is acceptable
- Adopt all necessary precautions
- Keep your employees informed
- Draw up your policy statement
- Revise it as necessary
- Show your employees your policy statement
- Remember it's up to you now.

16 Your employees' rights

Appointment □ Young persons □ Pregnancy and work □ Training □ Information □ Enforcing company rules □ Trade unions □ Checklist

All employees are entitled to safe conditions and freedom from health risks at work. They also have a duty to take reasonable care of themselves at work and of others who may be affected by the way in which they do their work. (See *Hiring and Firing* in this series.)

Appointment

There are few restrictions when appointing people. Obviously a heavy goods vehicle driver needs the appropriate licence; power-press setters, those who mount any kind of abrasive wheels, and divers must have the statutory training. If they have not already received this, you must arrange it before they undertake such work for you.

Disabled persons have the same rights as the able-bodied and you need to satisfy yourself that they will be safe at work and, for instance, in case of fire.

Young persons

These are males and females over compulsory school age but under 18 years of age. Do not expect them, particularly in their first job, to understand hazards with which more experienced workers are familiar. They will need careful – and perhaps repeated – instruction on basic safety requirements and 'works' rules. Make clear to them what they must not do (e.g. operate certain machines – or perhaps any for that matter). Arrange for them to be supervised closely, particularly at first.

Certain dangerous machines have been singled out for special attention. These include dough mixers, meat mincers and the office guillotine, even if hand-operated. No young person is allowed to work at any of the specified machines unless he or she has been fully instructed about its dangers and the relevant precautions. In addition, they must have either been sufficiently trained to work at any of the listed machines or be under the adequate supervision of someone with thorough knowledge and experience of the particular machine.

Pregnancy and work

A healthy pregnant woman can generally do most of the jobs that she was able to do before her pregnancy but there are a few points to note. First, there are statutory provisions which require pregnant women to be taken off work which would expose them to levels of lead or ionising radiations above certain limits. In addition, there are some jobs which involve possible hazards and pregnant women need special protection.

Exposure to some toxic substances like solvents, anaesthetic gases, hormone preparations and cytotoxic drugs, should be avoided, for instance, by nurses, pharmacists and laboratory workers. Teachers and nurses may be exposed to German measles and cytomegalovirus. Women workers in agriculture may be exposed to chlamydia psittaci and listeriosis, and pregnant women should not participate in lambing nor work in places where there is a low level of oxygen (e.g. some pig houses). Women manual workers should avoid heavy lifting and long periods of continuous standing at work. There are other situations which have to be avoided and in case of doubt medical advice should be obtained.

Training

Not only young persons but adults need training in health and safety. This may be 'on the job', i.e. at work, or 'off-the-job', for example at the local technical college. Health and safety should be taught as an integral part of training to do the job. The hazards of the work and of the working environment must be brought to the attention of employees. Those who work at processes involving lead, for instance, or who are otherwise exposed to lead have to be informed about the risks and precautions. Some machines like those used in woodworking can only be used lawfully by persons sufficiently trained and instructed in the dangers and precautions unless working under the adequate supervision of a person experienced in the working of the machine.

A sufficient number of employees should be trained in the use of fire extinguishers of the type you provide. Someone – preferably more than one person – should be trained in first aid.

Information

Allied to training is the giving of information, both verbal and written. An official poster *Health and Safety Law* has to be displayed at the place of work or a leaflet containing the same information has to be given to all employees. Copies are available from HMSO. Some pocket-size leaflets and cards are issued by HSE for the information of employees. Examples from many are:

- *Save Your Breath. Campaign against occupational lung disease – advice for employees.*
- *Save Your Skin. Occupational contact dermatitis.*
- *Beware of Noise.*
- *Safe Working with Small Dumpers.*
- *Safe Working with Overhead Travelling Cranes.*

(See also Chapter 19.)

Enforcing company rules

Every firm has some health and safety rules even if not written down. A few written rules are generally preferable and should be pithy and clear. Make sure that everyone knows and obeys the rules, and do not rely merely on notices. They are useful but only as a reminder of what employees have been told. Even so, some rules (e.g. against violence at work) are implied.

Disciplinary procedures

What happens when someone breaks the safety rules? This depends on the seriousness of the breach. For a minor one a verbal reprimand may suffice but you may have to invoke the formal disciplinary procedure as for other forms of wrong behaviour, i.e. the sequence

16

of (1) oral warning; (2) written warning; (3) final written warning, pointing out possible dismissal; (4) dismissal or suspension. Instant dismissal may sometimes be justified but you need to be very sure of your ground and act fairly.

An employee of a tank-cleaning company was working on the site of a well-known oil company which enforced rigid safety standards on its premises. One requirement was that anyone entering a tank had to wear breathing apparatus. The employee was seen about to enter a tank with his breathing apparatus slung on his shoulder and was dismissed. The man said to the Industrial Tribunal that he found it easier to work without wearing the apparatus and did not believe that there was a risk. But he admitted that he knew that he was risking his job. This dismissal was confirmed as fair.

In this case the failure was so serious a matter that no prior warnings were needed before dismissal. It is more usual to invoke the formal procedure but it is important always to allow the employee to explain his or her behaviour. Also rules must never be enforced in an arbitrary manner such as against one employee but not another in similar circumstances.

Constructive dismissal

The boot may be on the other foot if you as employer fail to play your part in safety. If you fail to provide something necessary for health and safety, the employee may resign and claim that he was forced to do so in effect because of your failure. This is known as *constructive dismissal,* and you would be financially liable for it.

A woman employed by a well-known company found that the goggles they provided were unsuitable. She complained to the management who failed to investigate the matter properly. Her complaint was bona fide but the employer's failure to investigate the matter was held to be a breach of contract. Her resignation was deemed to be constructive dismissal.

The underlying reason for constructive dismissal and dismissal by the employer is that there was a fundamental breach of the contract of employment by the other party.

Payment system

If you pay employees by some kind of incentive system, you will need to ensure that this does not encourage them to cut corners in safety. Workers have been known to remove machine guards, for instance, in order to speed up output and earn more money. The answer usually lies in discipline and supervision.

Trade unions

If you recognise a registered trade union, it may appoint safety representatives from among your employees. If so, it has to notify you in writing. Safety representatives have many functions, such as carrying out safety inspections, investigating accidents, representing the interests of the employees in matters concerning their health, safety and welfare at work, and to secure information from inspectors.

They are allowed time off with pay to do this and for attending certain training courses. They are expected to keep up-to-date with the health and safety requirements relating to the workplace.

Checklist

- Check the qualifications of new employees where appropriate
- Ensure the safety of disabled employees
- Train and supervise young persons carefully
- Ensure adults are trained and supervised as necessary
- Provide safety information for all employees
- Enforce company rules fairly
- Use the formal dismissal procedure where necessary
- Fulfil the safety standards and avoid cases of constructive dismissal
- Do not let pay incentives lower safety standards
- Cooperate with safety representatives if you have any

16

17 Maintenance work risks

Means of access and place of work □ Mechanical risks □
Welding □ Planned plant maintenance □ Wear and tear □
Hand tools □ Checklist

Maintenance work includes a wide range of activities, often in places difficult to reach such as a valve within a jungle of pipes. It would be a good idea if maintenance personnel came from a long line of acrobats at some establishments. Maintenance includes the repair, servicing, restoration, lubrication, cleaning of all types of plant, machinery, vehicles, structures and much else. There are opportunities for injury, such as:

- being caught up in an ungrateful machine after clearing a blockage without proper precautions;
- falling off ladders;
- toppling off roofs;
- dropping through fragile roofs;
- crashing through skylights;
- being trapped in lifts;
- being overcome by fumes or gases;
- being cut (e.g. on a saw) or being bruised by a faulty hammer.

If all else fails to maim, there is the chance of health problems from handling asbestos used perhaps as insulation material.

You have to accept prime responsibility for all this and need to check on the type of work which has to be done under your control. Certain common hazards may be singled out for further consideration:

- means of access and places of work;
- mechanical hazards;
- welding.

Means of access and place of work

A ladder may be the means of access or the place of work itself. It should be suitable for the job in hand (e.g. not too short) and should be properly secured (e.g. by lashing). (See also Chapter 4.)

The place of work for maintenance may be just about anywhere: in, on or under plant, machinery, vehicles, buildings and so on. Review the places where such work has to be done, however infrequently, and you may find some awkward spots for access. So try to improve matters by altering the layout and other relevant features.

Buildings

The maintenance of buildings by its nature often takes place for periods of short duration so that there is a tendency not to bother with scaffolding or other access equipment at each job. The best solution is to provide permanent walkways to give access (e.g. on roofs). In cases where a safety belt or harness provides the only effective means of protection, built-in permanent anchorages may be the answer (e.g. for window cleaners).

Another feature which affects the way the work is done is that the maintenance is necessary precisely because the building has deteriorated. This is especially important when access to a roof is required. Roofing material, non-fragile when installed, may deteriorate in time and, whilst externally looking no different, it may be lethal to step on. Fragile panels in a roof may be indistinguishable from the rest of the roof through painting, weathering, or the deposit of dirt or dust.

Two brothers were sent on to a roof to clean the roof lights which had been painted, like the roof itself, with bituminous paint. The first brother, not identifying the roof lights, fell through one but fortunately landed astride a metal stanchion in the factory. He then proceeded to climb back on to the roof to warn his brother of the danger but was too late. His brother fell to his death through another roof light.

There may be difficulties in carrying out maintenance in buildings such as blocks of flats, where there are residents. Scaffolders may not be able to use the windows for through ties – and, of course, the residents will need protection, e.g. from falling objects. In addition, it is more than usually necessary to take precautions against children scrambling up the scaffolding or otherwise getting into danger.

There are special precautions to be taken when someone has to enter a confined space where there is a risk of being overcome by gases or fumes or oxygen deficiency. Confined spaces include chambers, tanks, vats, pits, wells, pipes, flues, excavations and similar places. Gases or fumes may be present as residual material left in the sludge (e.g. in an 'empty' tank); or created by the use of an internal combustion engine used to drive a pump in a well; or from the escape of gas from a pipe; and in a host of other ways.

The precautions centre on what is known as a 'permit-to-work system' which is discussed in Chapter 8.

Mechanical risks

Risks associated with machines are discussed in Chapter 12 and of these a number arise in maintenance work and in general similar precautions have to be taken.

Welding

Between them, electric arc and gas welding present a medley of problems:

- damage to the eyes;
- burns to the skin;
- electric shock;
- fume and gas inhalation;
- fire;
- explosion.

Not only the welder's eyes are exposed to the electric arc, but those of persons nearby. The welder's skin is also at risk. Electric shock is another possibility to be taken seriously. Fumes and gases may be produced by the process itself, either from the metal being welded or the electrodes being used. Medical experts are not agreed about the long-term health effects, if any, of welding. Sparks given off are quite good at setting things on fire and a sudden explosion can be staged by trying to weld an 'empty' tank which has contained

17

flammable liquids. Even when apparently empty, a tank may contain a residue of flammables. Careful preparatory procedures are needed.

In one factory a workman had to remove the tops of some drums which had contained petrol. Relying on the nose – a quick sniff indicated all as clear – the man applied the welding torch to the drum. A muffled explosion resulted, his clothing started to burn and the drum and contents flew some distance to become flaming piles on the floor. No precautions had been taken and it was found that heavier petroleum fractions had been secreted in the drum's seams, ready to explode on the application of heat.

Precautions

Protective goggles and face screens where appropriate, suitable gloves and apron protect the welder. Screening off the welding area is needed to protect outsiders from 'eye-flash' injury which can happen as the result of one glance at the arc. Electricity safeguards according to statutory standard are always essential. This is a matter for expert advice. Fumes and gases may often be removed by good natural ventilation but sometimes mechanical extraction is required.

It is imperative that employees receive proper training and instruction and, as necessary, supervision. Knowledge of the dangers does not come naturally.

A youth was cutting through an oil-filled pipe. As his cutting torch cut through the last portion of the metal, the hot oil squirted out and ignited, burning his face and setting his clothes on fire. He was badly burned and permanently disfigured.

Planned plant maintenance

Some items of plant like lifts have to have regular statutory examination and maintenance but all plant and machinery needs it. Some of the main benefits from a planned system of maintenance are:

- work injuries on faulty machines are reduced;
- plant availability is increased;
- production is less likely to be suddenly interrupted;

- the standard of maintenance is higher;
- better use of labour force is facilitated because of reduced breakdowns;
- machinery and plant last longer;
- machinery and plant maintain their value better.

Those who undertake maintenance and associated examination and inspection duties have their own hazards to face and it is easy to become complacent about them.

A passenger lift was being installed in a commercial building under construction and had almost been completed. A lift engineer entered the pit without isolating a second lift and was struck by the balance weight of the neighbouring lift.

It is essential that anyone who is working in a lift shaft shall be protected from contact with adjacent lifts which are still in operation. A safe procedure should be drawn up, taught and followed always.

Wear and tear

Every working machine must be subject to wear and tear and deterioration in performance may be insidious and undetected. Only regular checking and maintenance can keep machinery in tip-top condition. These remarks also apply equally to wear and tear of safety devices. Interlocking devices may develop hidden weaknesses and automatic devices can become defective and cease to afford protection for the operator. Even fixed guards grow slack and need regular examination.

In making adjustments to machines it is often overlooked that there is no exemption for maintenance personnel and they must use safeguards even when trying out the machine afterwards. Records of adequate details must be kept for some plant and machinery under specific legislation but all should now be logged carefully and legibly. You have a duty to maintain plant and machines in good and safe condition in all cases. For your own purposes as well as to satisfy the professional interest of inspectors you should keep systematic records. When a particular register is required according to regulations (e.g. for power presses) it must be used.

17

Hand tools

These, too, must obviously be properly maintained in the interests of the work as well as of safety. Points which particularly need to be borne in mind for commonly used tools are:

- **hammers** – avoid split, broken or loose shafts and worn or chipped heads; heads must be properly secured to the shaft;
- **files** should always have a proper handle in good condition;
- **chisels** – the cutting edge should be kept sharpened to the correct angle and steps taken to prevent mushroom heads;
- **screwdrivers** must never be used as chisels, and hammers should never be used on them. Avoid split handles;
- **spanners** – avoid splayed jaws and scrap any which show signs of stripping. Keep a sufficient range of sizes to prevent improvising.

Checklist

- Maintenance of all kinds has a safety aspect
- Ensure safe means of access
- Ensure a safe place of work
- Use a PTW system where appropriate
- Take precautions when maintaining machinery (e.g. isolate electrically-operated machinery)
- Note that there are a number of risks with welding
- Protect the welder's eyes
- Protect others from eye-flash injury
- Ensure electrical precautions are correct
- Prevent sparks igniting material
- Ensure 'empty' drums are safe before applying heat

18 Enforcement and the cost of failure to comply

To whom is a duty owed? □ The HSC □ The HSE □ Local
authority inspectors □ Powers □ Issue of notices □
Prosecution □ Penalties □ Manslaughter □ Employer's
liability □ Checklist

Health and safety legislation is part of the criminal law. As an
employer, manufacturer, designer, supplier, importer, occupier, etc.
you may have duties. As an individual you have, too.

To whom is a duty owed?

The safety of people such as customers as well as employees is covered
by this legislation. Penalties can be severe for contraventions (see
p. 132). In addition, you owe a common law duty to employees
and others for whom you should provide reasonably safe conditions.
If any of them is injured, he or she may claim damages (money)
to compensate them. In the case of employees it is compulsory to
have insurance (employer's liability).

The HSC

Those letters stand for Health and Safety Commission, the policy-
making body which gives general directions to the HSE (Health and
Safety Executive). You are unlikely to have any direct dealings with
the HSC.

The HSE

Although the underlying philosophy in health and safety is one of
self-regulation, in practice a fairly elaborate system of enforcement
is necessary. There are two kinds of inspectorates: those of central

government and those of local authorities. There are six inspectorates in the HSE:

- Factories (the largest);
- Agriculture;
- Mines and quarries;
- Nuclear;
- Explosives;
- Railway.

Fire authorities have important specialist duties but are not part of the HSE. The HSE itself acts as agent for the Ministry of Agriculture, Fisheries and Food under the Food and Environment Protection legislation. There is also collaboration with various government departments on matters of joint interest.

Organisation

In addition to the headquarters organisation, the HSE has 21 geographic areas, each with a National Industry Group (NIG) centred on it. (See Appendix.) All field inspectors aim to apply the same standards but look to the NIG for guidance (e.g. on new technical problems).

Local authority inspectors

Whilst HSE inspectors generally deal with manufacturing and major or complex types of workplaces, local authorities are particularly involved with offices, wholesale and retail distribution and service industries such as hotels and catering. Many small firms will be subject to inspection by local authorities. The nominated inspectors are usually Environmental Health Officers (EHOs). Liaison is maintained with the HSE as the 'lead' authority on health and safety.

Powers

All inspectors have the same powers under the law:

- to enter your premises at almost any time;
- to inspect them;
- to investigate accidents;

- to take photographs, recordings and measurements;
- to examine relevant documents;
- to take samples;
- to order the dismantling of dangerous articles;
- to take away articles and substances;
- to question anyone on the premises;
- to require them to sign a written declaration;
- to require facilities and assistance for carrying out their duties;
- to issue Prohibition Notices and Improvement Notices;
- to prosecute.

Inspection policy

In spite of this formidable list, it is official policy to promote compliance with good standards, to advise rather than prosecute. Inspectors are ready to discuss your problems although lack of funds does not excuse you from providing safe conditions. The HSE issue safety leaflets for employers, employees and others to give information and advice.

Issue of notices

Inspectors can issue two kinds of written notice, both 'on the spot':

- Improvement Notices
- Prohibition Notices

They can be addressed to any person, individual or corporate, but most are issued to employers.

In one case, so an anecdote says, an inspector issued a Prohibition Notice to an employee, forbidding him to move his car in the company car park. It was, in the inspector's opinion, too dangerous to use on the premises.

Although no prior warning is needed before issuing either kind of notice, an inspector will discuss the matter and any problems you may have, before issuing it. Both kinds are legal documents and are to be taken seriously.

18

Improvement Notices

If you have not acted on an inspector's advice given at a previous visit, you may well receive one of these. These notices require the employer (or other person addressed) to make specified improvements by a certain date which will be more than 21 days hence. This period is allowed for you to appeal to an industrial tribunal if you so wish. Few appeal and of those who do, few succeed. To a small firm, the hassle and time involved are deterrents.

If, for instance, you are required to fit a certain safeguard within three months but the supplier informs you that he cannot supply within that period, tell the inspector and seek an extension of the time. But do not wait until the three months have elapsed before doing so, for the inspector is unlikely to be able to help you. Failure to comply with such a notice (which is based on an alleged breach of the law) may land you in court.

Prohibition Notices

These are even more severe documents and do not depend on an alleged breach of legislation. An inspector may issue one whenever he or she considers that there is a risk of serious personal injury or health risk. Some notices take effect immediately but some are 'deferred'. The former may order you to cease an operation immediately and you must comply.

Failure to comply with such notices is one of the most serious offences under the legislation, so do what it says. You must expect the inspector to come back to check compliance with the notice.

A director of three construction companies was sentenced to 18 months' imprisonment, suspended for two years, after one of the companies had been involved in asbestos removal without a statutory asbestos licence and in contravention of a Prohibition Notice. He was also fined £1,200 for various other offences. The fines would have been higher, said the Judge, but he had been convinced that the director was devoid of assets.

You have a right to appeal within 21 days but, unlike the Improvement Notice, you must comply immediately.

Some key differences

Improvement Notice	Prohibition Notice
• Orders a specified improvement	• Bans something
• Requires this by a certain date	• Generally operative immediately
• Need not comply for 21 days	• Does not allow this delay
• Breach is a summary offence	• Breach is an indictable offence

Prosecution

Although inspectors prefer to secure compliance without prosecuting, they could be sometimes compelled to take legal action, for instance, if

- a serious offence has been revealed by an accident;
- you have persistently contravened the legislation;
- you have failed to comply with a notice.

Legal proceedings are usually taken in the magistrates' court (in England and Wales) but more serious indictable offences may be taken in the crown court (trial by jury). In Scotland the accused has no right to opt for trial by jury. The inspector who proposes to prosecute submits a report, with supporting evidence, to higher authority for approval (e.g. the Area Director in the HSE). In Scotland, this report is submitted to the Procurator Fiscal who decides whether to proceed.

Any person, individual or corporate, may be prosecuted. In most cases it is the employer who is prosecuted but there are exceptions.

Two employees in a furniture factory were fooling around. One, a man of 56, threw a hammer at the head of the other, a 17-year-old youth. The teenager threw a cartridge of staples at the older man. Neither intended to injure the other as it was just horseplay. But the inspector prosecuted both – successfully – for failing to take reasonable care for another person at work.

18

Penalties

The maximum fine in a magistrates' court is currently £1,000 on each count. In the crown court, fines are unlimited and for the more serious offences, such as failing to comply with a Prohibition Notice, up to two years' imprisonment may be imposed. Costs may also be awarded. Appeals are possible to the general legal system but you will need the necessary funds!

Manslaughter

The first manslaughter case (as far as is known) in connection with health and safety legislation was on 1 December, 1989 when a one-year prison sentence, suspended for two years, was imposed on a company director. The case arose from an accident at the workplace.

At the company's factory, an employee was killed in a plastics crumbling machine. Both the HSE and the police investigated the matter. Two of the directors (brothers) were prosecuted for unlawful killing and various other offences. One director was found guilty of manslaughter and both of various other offences. Fines totalling £47,000 were also imposed as well as the suspended prison sentence.

As the HSC has said: 'The case brings home the severe view that the courts are beginning to take of derelictions of this kind'.

Employer's liability

It is a criminal offence to fail to have employer's liability insurance. If an employee suffers injury or damage to health owing to your firm's negligence, he may make a claim for damages (money) against you. The insurance company will take over and deal with the claim. If they decide to fight it in the court, you may have to attend to give evidence.

You may receive claims from customers or others who are injured, allegedly by your firm's negligence. For this you should have suitable insurance also.

Checklist

- Avoid breaches of the legislation
- Inspectors have considerable powers
- Never ignore any notices which they issue
- Appeals are available but involve hassle
- Any person or firm may be prosecuted
- You must take out employer's liability insurance

18

19 Essential documents, reports and notices

Information, advice and warning ☐ Licences and certificates ☐ Records of statutory examination ☐ Health records ☐ Notification ☐ Sources ☐ Checklist

It is inevitable that there should be many documents associated with health and safety at work. They have a range of purposes and are of various kinds which may be broadly classified under the following headings:

- information, advice and warning;
- licences and certificates;
- records of plant examination;
- health records;
- notification.

Information, advice and warning

Various notices should be posted up at the workplace. These include: a copy of safety regulations applying to the premises (e.g. Woodworking Machines Regulations); at all places of work, a notice entitled *Health and Safety Law. What You Should Know* should be posted up or, alternatively, a leaflet copy should be given to every employee. If you opt for this alternative, do not forget to give a copy to every new recruit in the future.

Reference documents aimed at employers include a series of detailed technical documents known as *Guidance Notes*. Codes of practice associated with regulations are also available as well as short leaflets offering practical advice in potted form. These include *Health and Safety in Small Clothing Factories* and *Review Your Occupational Health Needs. Employer's Guide.*

Warning notices for posting up in appropriate premises include *Warning: Danger of Explosion* in oil storage-tanks fitted with immersed heaters. More warnings today are issued in pocket card-form to be

19

given to employees. Examples are *Wear Your Badge* (for radiation workers), *Asbestos Alert for the Construction Worker* and *Safe Working with Overhead Crane. Driver's Guide.*

Licences and certificates

Licences needed for the storage of petroleum and certain petroleum products are obtained from the local authority. A Certificate of Means of Escape in Case of Fire is needed by many − probably most − small firms. Application should be made to the fire authority or, in some cases, the fire brigade. A certificate indicating that a policy of insurance has been obtained covering employer's liability should be displayed.

For certain work, individual employees have to be trained and certified by you as employer as you appoint them to undertake such jobs as tool setting at power presses and mounting of abrasive wheels.

Records of statutory examination

Lifts, cranes, pressurised plant like steam boilers and air receivers have to be periodically examined by a competent person, usually an insurance company engineer or surveyor. All reports have to be kept on file.

It is compulsory to maintain all plant, machinery and equipment in a safe condition. Generally this means regular routine examination and maintenance for which adequate records should be kept.

Health records

For certain occupations where there is a special health risk, periodical medical examinations are required (e.g. for diving and certain work involving exposure to lead). Health registers have to be kept. Advice may be obtained from EMAS.

Notifications

Certain important matters have to be reported to the inspector such as:

- opening a new factory;
- reportable accidents;
- reportable dangerous occurrences;
- certain work with asbestos.

The requirements for reporting accidents and dangerous occurrences are set out in the booklet *Reporting Injury or a Dangerous Occurrence.* Any accident to employees, self-employed people, people being trained for employment, visitors to the premises and members of the public must be notified if it

- is fatal;
- causes serious injury (as set out in the booklet);
- leads to over 24 hours in hospital;
- causes more than three days' incapacity.

Form 2508 must be completed for each person and, in addition, for the first three types, notification must be given by the quickest practical means (e.g. telephone).

Sources

The major documents are available from branches of HMSO. Leaflets and pocket cards may be obained from HSE. To keep up-to-date, a modest subscription will provide you with the HSC's *Newsletter* regularly.

Checklist

- Check what documents apply to your activities
- Obtain, issue and use them as appropriate
- Make sure that you have any necessary licences and certificates
- Keep records of plant examinations and maintenance
- Notify accidents promptly
- Keep up-to-date

19

Appendix:
Area office
information services

Area offices

Members of the public who need advice on any aspect of the Health and Safety at Work Act 1974 should enquire at any of the 20 area offices listed below.

In each area office there are groups of inspectors specialising in the specific industries to be found in the area. One office may have between five and ten of these industry groups, which are linked nationally on an industry basis to permit an interchange of information on common working techniques and practices.

The basic functions of an inspector require him to spend most of his time away from his office, but each group has an administrative support group, who will be the first point of contact for an enquirer. The office staff will accept messages and enquiries for technical or interpretative advice, complaints, etc., which will be referred to the inspector as quickly as possible. Except in the case of an emergency, it will be unusual for an inspector to make an immediate response. If a visit is necessary, it will have to be accommodated within the inspector's programme, which may take some time to arrange; however, a reply or a visit will normally be made.

Useful addresses

South West

Inter City House
Mitchell Lane
Bristol BS1 6AN
0272 290681

Local authorities

Avon, Cornwall, Devon,
Gloucestershire, Somerset,
Isles of Scilly.

South

Priestley House
Priestley Road
Basingstoke RG24 9NW
0256 473181

Local authorities

Berkshire, Dorset,
Hampshire, Isle of Wight,
Wiltshire.

South East

3 East Grinstead House
London Road
East Grinstead
West Sussex RH19 1RR
0342 326922

Local authorities

Kent, Surrey, East Sussex,
West Sussex.

London North

Maritime House
1 Linton Road
Barking
Essex IG11 8HF
081 594 5522

Local authorities

Barking and Dagenham,
Barnet, Brent, Camden,
Ealing, Enfield, Hackney,
Haringey, Harrow, Havering,
Islington, Newham,
Redbridge, Tower Hamlets,
Waltham Forest.

London South

1 Long Lane
London SE1 4PG
071 407 8911

Local authorities

Bexley, Bromley, City of
London, Croydon,
Greenwich, Hammersmith
and Fulham, Hillingdon,
Hounslow, Kensington and
Chelsea, Kingston, Lambeth,
Lewisham, Merton,
Richmond, Southwark,
Sutton, Wandsworth,
Westminster.

East Anglia

39 Baddow Road
Chelmsford
Essex CM2 0HL
0245 284661

Local authorities

Essex except the London
Borough of Essex covered by
London N, Norfolk, Suffolk.

Northern Home Counties

14 Cardiff Road
Luton
Beds LU1 1PP
0582 34121

Local authorities

Bedfordshire,
Buckinghamshire,
Cambridgeshire,
Hertfordshire.

East Midlands

Belgrave House
1 Greyfriars
Northampton NN1 2BS
0604 21233

Local authorities

Leicestershire,
Northamptonshire,
Oxfordshire, Warwickshire.

West Midlands

McLaren Building
2 Masshouse Circus
Queensway
Birmingham B4 7NP
021 200 2299

Local authorities

West Midlands.

Wales

Brunel House
2 Fitzalan Road
Cardiff CF2 1SH
0222 473777

Local authorities

Clwyd, Dyfed, Gwent,
Gwynedd, Mid Glamorgan,
Powys, South Glamorgan,
West Glamorgan.

Marches

The Marches House
Midway
Newcastle-under-Lyme

Staffs. ST5 1DT
0782 717181

Local authorities

Hereford and Worcester,
Shropshire, Staffordshire.

North Midlands

Birkbeck House
Trinity Square
Nottingham NG1 4AU
0602 470712

Local authorities

Derbyshire, Lincolnshire,
Nottinghamshire.

South Yorkshire

Sovereign House
40 Silver Street
Sheffield S1 2ES
0742 739081

Local authorities

Humberside, South
Yorkshire.

West and North Yorkshire

8 St Pauls Street
Leeds LS1 2LE
0532 446191

Local authorities

North Yorkshire, West
Yorkshire.

Greater Manchester

Quay House
Quay Street
Manchester M3 3JB
061 831 7111

Local authorities

Greater Manchester.

Merseyside

The Triad
Stanley Road
Bootle L20 3PG
051 922 7211

Local authorities

Cheshire, Merseyside.

North West

Victoria House
Ormskirk Road
Preston PR1 1HH
0772 59321

Local authorities

Cumbria, Lancashire.

North East

Arden House
Regent Centre
Regent Farm Road
Gosforth
Newcastle-upon-Tyne
NE3 3JN
091 284 8448

Local authorities

Cleveland, Durham,
Northumberland, Tyne and
Wear.

Scotland East

Belford House
59 Belford Road
Edinburgh EH4 3UE
031 225 1313

Local authorities

Borders, Central, Fife,
Grampian, Highland,
Lothian, Tayside, and the
island areas of Orkney and
Shetland

Scotland

314 St Vincent Street
Glasgow G3 8XG
041 204 2646

Local authorities

Dumfries and Galloway,
Strathclyde, and the Western
Isles.

Appx

Public enquiry points

The HSE Library and Information Services have three Public Enquiry Points located as follows:

Health and Safety Executive
Library and Information Services
Broad Lane
Sheffield S3 7HQ
Tel: 0742 752539
Telex: 54556
Fax: 0742 755792

Health and Safety Executive
Library and Information Services
St Hugh's House
Stanley Precinct
Trinity Road
Bootle
Merseyside L20 3QY
Tel: 051-951 4381
Telex: 628235
Fax: 051-922 5394

Health and Safety Executive
Library and Information Services
Baynards House
1 Chepstow Place
Westbourne Grove
London W2 4TF
Tel: 071 221 0870
Telex: 25683
Fax: 071 727 2254

Prestel

HSE Library and Information Services is an information provider on Prestel. Free leaflets and press releases can be ordered and messages can also be sent to HSE. Lead frame 50040.

HSELINE

HSE's publicly available database of references to occupational health and safety literature is mounted on two host services. Apply to above addresses for details.

Publications

Publications are sold through HMSO bookshops, except for such items as leaflets which are available free from area offices and the Public Enquiry Points. HMSO bookshops are listed below.

The Publications in Series: List is published free of charge twice per annum. It lists all titles published by the Health and Safety Executive available from area offices and Public Enquiry Points.

Lists of pre- and post-Health and Safety at Work Act legislation and also lists of forms can be supplied from the Public Enquiry Points.

List of HMSO bookshops

49 High Holborn, London WC1V 6HB
71 Lothian Road, Edinburgh EH3 9AZ
9–21 Princess Street, Manchester M60 8AS
Southey House, Wine Street, Bristol BS1 2BQ
258 Broad Street, Birmingham B1 2HE
80 Chichester Street, Belfast BT1 4JY

Government publications are also available through booksellers.

Index

Related titles from Pitman:

First Aid in the Workplace
Lord Taylor of Harlow and Patricia M Elliot

This book has for many years been recommended for all those
on first-aid training courses. It has now been extensively
updated with the assistance of Dr Patricia Elliot, an
experienced medical director in occupational health.

The test is a well-structured practical guide with health
topics arranged in a logical order and numerous checklists for
ease of learning. It restricts itself to that area of first aid which
first aiders at work must know if they are to carry out their
duties effectively, thus ensuring that the first aider is not
confused by detail unrelated to first aid at work and not
encouraged to carry out treatment best left to a trained doctor.

Recent concerns such as coping with the risk of AIDS
infection are covered. A separate chapter offers helpful
guidance to first-aid trainers.

'. . . offers in practical handbook format and clear, concise
terms, a really down-to-earth, well-illustrated text for first-aid
trainers and trainees, as well as workplace first aiders.'
Occupational Health and Safety

Published 1988, 176 pages, Paper, ISBN 0 273 02858 8

RoSPA Health and Safety Practice
M Dewis and J W Stranks

A clear and comprehensive introduction to the practice of health and safety at work. Published in association with the Royal Society for the Prevention of Accidents, it is an ideal source of information and guidance for health and safety practitioners and those studying for a wide range of professional institute examinations.

It contains over 40 chapters covering the effective prevention, working environment, occupational health and application of health and safety management, law, accident hygiene, human behaviour and safety technology.

'An excellent book which should improve the professionalism of health and safety practitioners significantly.' *Occupational Health and Safety*

Published 1986, 512 pages, Paper, ISBN 0 273 02599 6

These books are available from all good bookshops. In case of difficulty, contact: Pitman Publishing, 128 Long Acre, London WC2E 9AN. Tel: 071 379 7383